Name _____

Directions Say the name of each picture. Write the letter that stands for the beginning sound.

1.	2.	3.	4.	5.
6.	7.	8.	9.	10.
11.	12.	13.	14.	15.
16.	17.	18.	19.	20.
21.	22.	23.	24.	25.

LESSON 1: Initial consonants in short vowel words

1

Directions Say the name of each picture. Write the letter that stands for the consonant sound you hear in the middle of the picture name.

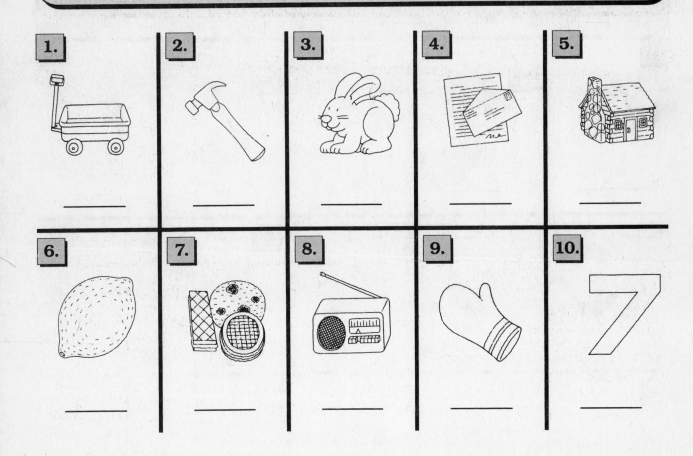

1.	2.	3.	4.	5.
____	____	____	____	____

6.	7.	8.	9.	10.
____	____	____	____	____

Directions Read each sentence. Complete the unfinished word by writing the middle consonant.

1. My cousin Raphael is a fo___est ranger.

2. He lives in a ca___in in the woods.

3. We tra___el to see him each summer.

4. Raphael takes my family for hi___es.

5. He points out interesting ani___als.

6. I have seen many beau___iful trees.

7. My sister takes photos with her ca___era.

8. We have learned to avoid poison i___y.

9. My favorite time is the eve___ing.

10. We build a campfire and tell sto___ies.

2

LESSON 1: Medial consonants

Name _____ _____

Directions Write the name of each picture on the line.

1. _____

2. _____

3. _____

4. _____

5. _____

6. _____

7. _____

8. _____

Directions Complete each sentence with a word from the box.

1. Scott is learning to _____ .

2. Each morning he makes his _____ .

3. He usually makes _____ and eggs.

4. Scott fries the bacon in a _____ .

5. It is easy to make toast in the _____ .

6. Scott likes to _____ orange juice.

7. He would like to _____ other foods.

8. Perhaps he will bake _____ muffins.

bacon
make
pan
bran
toaster
drink
breakfast
cook

3

LESSON 2: Final consonants

1. The Woods a___e shopping for a pet.

2. Jacy would like to have a pu___py.

3. She will do her par___ to care for it.

4. The Woods visit a sho___ called Patti's Puppies.

5. Jacy spots a puppy she li___es.

6. She rushes to its cage to take a loo___.

7. "What ki___d of puppy is this?" Jacy asks.

8. "Tha___ is a Lhasa Apso," replies Patti.

9. "I've hear___ of this breed," says Mrs. Wood.

10. "Lhasas are native ___o Tibet."

11. "They don't gro___ very tall," says Patti.

12. "This pup will be about fif___een inches."

13. "It also will grow a heavy coa___."

14. Mr. Wood knows thi___ breed is friendly.

15. Patti adds, "These do___s can be stubborn!"

16. She says Lhasas o___ce were trained to guard royalty.

17. "Today anyone can ow___ one!" Patti says.

18. Jacy want___ to help pay for the puppy.

19. She puts her money on the counte___.

20. Patti suggests the Woods buy dog foo___, too.

21. She also finds a leash and a colla___.

22. The fa___ily is soon ready to go home.

23. Everyone than___s Patti for her help.

24. Jacy is thrilled with her ne___ pet.

25. She decides to na___e it Snuggles.

LESSON 2: Test: Consonants

Name _____

Rule If a word or syllable has only one vowel, and it comes at the beginning or between two consonants, the vowel usually stands for the short sound.

EXAMPLES

ax   bag
is   fox

Directions Circle each picture whose name has the short sound of the vowel at the left. Then write the name of each picture you circled.

1.
a

_____ _____ _____ _____

2.
i

_____ _____ _____ _____

3.
u

_____ _____ _____ _____

4.
o

_____ _____ _____ _____

5.
e

_____ _____ _____ _____

Directions Draw a line to connect each word in the first column with a word in the second column that has the same vowel sound.

1.

sack	cub
cut	lock
pill	lamp
doll	yell
kept	slip

2.

pump	black
sand	hopped
dill	club
crept	went
block	miss

3.

slim	eggs
spell	boxed
trucked	picnic
job	wax
ant	hug

Directions Read each sentence, and find the picture that goes with it. Write the number of the sentence under the picture. Then circle every word in which you hear a short vowel sound.

1. A big bug crept under the rug.

2. Open the big lock on the box.

3. The funny fish can jog and hop.

4. A hot pot sat on a log.

5. Meg met Peg at the jet.

6. The silly egg had on a wig.

7. Jim got a lump when he bumped the lamp.

8. Bill's pup has a bell on his neck.

6 LESSON 3: Short vowels

Name _____

1. Our team earned a ___ in the tournament.

   spot ○ pots ○ speed ○

2. We rode the team ___ to the game.

   fuss ○ bus ○ ban ○

3. Jesse is at ___.

   cap ○ bet ○ bat ○

4. It's a base ___!

   sit ○ hot ○ hit ○

5. We cheer as Jesse ___ first base.

   tags ○ tugs ○ rags ○

6. The pitcher squints in the ___.

   fun ○ fad ○ sun ○

7. He pitches to our ___ batter.

   net ○ next ○ text ○

8. Katie misses the first ___.

   pitch ○ witch ○ hatch ○ ✓

9. She ___ for a minute.

   reads ○ bests ○ rests ○

10. The pitcher winds ___ and throws.

    up ○ at ○ but ○

11. Katie swings at a ___ ball.

    fest ○ fast ○ flag ○

12. The bat connects with a ___.

    crack ○ creek ○ stack ○

13. The ball sails over the ___ of the fence.

    top ○ crock ○ tap ○

14. It's a home ___!

    run ○ runt ○ ran ○

15. Our team ___ won the game.

    did ○ dog ○ has ○

16. We ___ a party to celebrate.

    hit ○ had ○ hid ○

Directions Circle the name of each picture.

Hint Some words look like they should follow the short-vowel rule, but don't. If a short vowel sound doesn't work, try a long vowel sound.

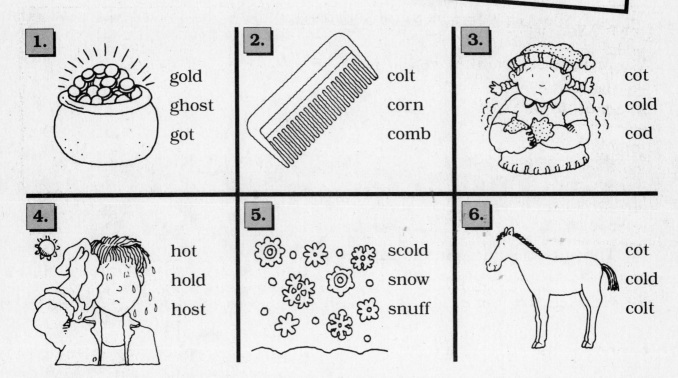

1.
gold
ghost
got

2.
colt
corn
comb

3.
cot
cold
cod

4.
hot
hold
host

5.
scold
snow
snuff

6.
cot
cold
colt

Directions Complete each sentence with a word from the box.

1. Please give me a _____ about the party.

2. Who is on the guest _____?

3. _____ our whole class be there?

4. Do you plan to _____ the list in class?

5. You will be a great _____!

6. Let's decorate the cake with _____ icing.

7. I hope it won't be too _____ outside.

8. We won't be allowed to _____ indoors.

9. Carrie is sure to _____ a prize.

10. She is the _____ runner in our class.

gold
best
hint
post
cold
list
win
run
Will
host

Name _____

Long-Vowel Rule 1 If a one-syllable word has two vowels, the first vowel usually stands for the long sound and the second vowel is silent.

EXAMPLES

rain	kite
cane	jeep

Long-Vowel Rule 2 If a word or syllable has one vowel and it comes at the end of the word or syllable, the vowel usually stands for the long sound.

EXAMPLES

we	go
cupid	pony

1.

_____

2.

_____

3.

_____

4.

_____

5.

_____

6.

_____

7.

_____

8.

_____

9.

_____

10.

_____

11.

_____

12.

_____

Directions Circle each picture whose name has the long sound of the vowel at the left. Then write the name of each picture you circled.

Long Vowel Rule 1 If a syllable has two vowels, the first vowel usually stands for the long sound and the second is silent.

1. a

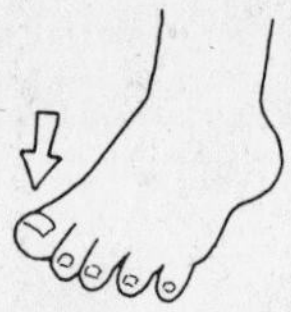

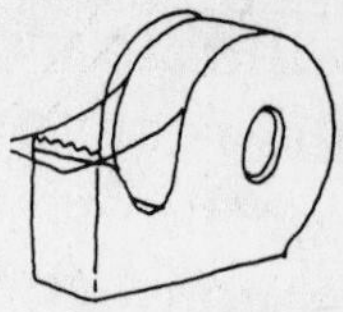

_____ _____ _____ _____

2. i

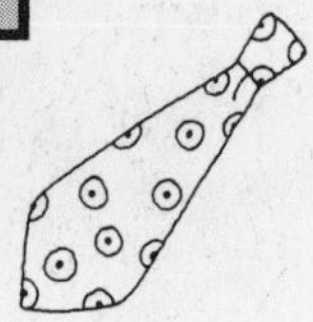

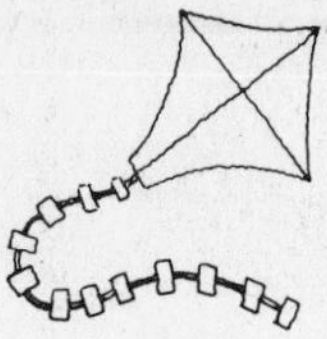

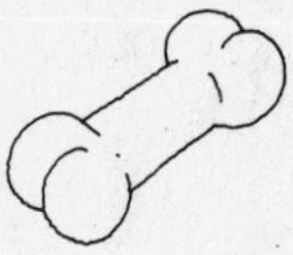

_____ _____ _____ _____

3. u

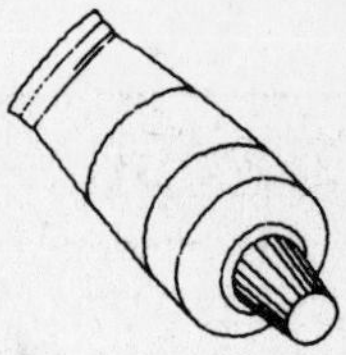

_____ _____ _____ _____

4. o

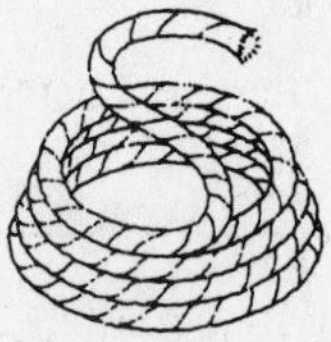

_____ _____ _____ _____

5. e

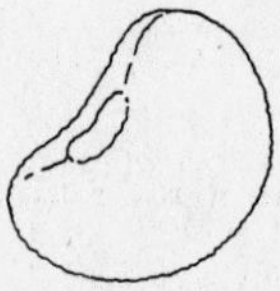

_____ _____ _____ _____

10

LESSON 5: Long vowels

Name _____

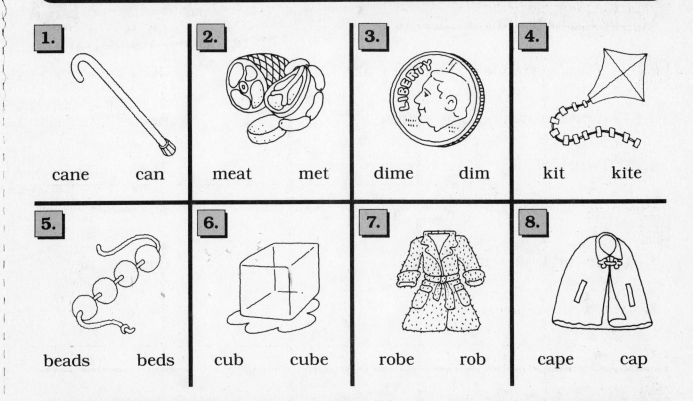

1.	2.	3.	4.
cane can	meat met	dime dim	kit kite
5.	6.	7.	8.
beads beds	cub cube	robe rob	cape cap

Directions Complete each sentence with a word that **rhymes** with one of the words in parentheses. The first letter of each unfinished word is given. Then circle each word in the sentences in which you hear a long vowel sound.

1. We are planning a d_____ at the beach.   (me, may)

2. It will be an escape from this h_____.   (mate, meat)

3. I can't s_____ in the sun too long.   (tray, treat)

4. I will be sure to wear a sun s_____.   (groan, green)

5. Mom wants to sail in the b_____.   (goat, greet)

6. Sheila h_____ Dad will take her fishing.   (reeds, ropes)

7. We all like to r_____ along the shore.   (foam, free)

8. When we walk, we k_____ our heads down.   (sheep, shape)

9. We l_____ to look for shells.   (spoke, spike)

10. I can't w_____ to get there.   (bait, beet)

1. My neighbor June is ___.

    bleed   blind
    ○   ○

2. ___ keeps a guide dog named Duke.

    June   Jeep
    ○   ○

3. Several ___ can become guide dogs.

    brides   breeds
    ○   ○

4. ___ include boxers and retrievers.

    Tries   These
    ○   ○

5. German shepherds are ___ guide dogs.

    fine   feet
    ○   ○

6. June and Duke walk each ___.

    die   day
    ○   ○

7. ___ wears a harness.

    Duke   Duck
    ○   ○

8. June ___ it firmly.

    hides   holds
    ○   ○

9. Duke walks first and ___ the way.

    leads   rides
    ○   ○

10. Duke stops at each curb and ___.

    writes   waits
    ○   ○

11. He does not ___ until he is told.

    tea   go
    ○   ○

12. June might ___, "Right."

    say   sue
    ○   ○

13. Then Duke goes on his ___.

    why   way
    ○   ○

14. Duke has been well ___.

    trained   tried
    ○   ○

15. His training lasted ___ months.

    fate   five
    ○   ○

16. I ___ to see Duke with June.

    lake   like
    ○   ○

17. They make a good ___!

    tame   team
    ○   ○

Name _____

Directions Find the name for each picture in the box. Write the picture name on the line.

Rule When **c** is followed by **e, i,** or **y,** the **c** is usually soft and has the /s/ sound.

center	fence	bicycle	lace	cents
car	pencil	cute	camel	cymbals
cane	circus	cereal	celery	candy

1. _____

2. _____

3. _____

4. _____

5. _____

6. _____

7. _____

8. _____

Directions Complete the paragraph with words from the box above.

Cynthia rode her _____ to Carol's house. Then she and Carol went to a shopping _____. Cynthia got _____ curtains for her room. In the parking lot, a little _____ was taking place. The girls saw two clowns playing the _____. They also saw a _____ with two humps. With her last ten _____, Carol bought a sharp new _____.

1. engine _____
2. cage _____
3. rigid _____
4. huge _____
5. orange _____
6. stingy _____
7. magic _____
8. sugar _____
9. giraffe _____
10. stage _____
11. guest _____
12. gas _____
13. game _____
14. badge _____
15. bug _____

Directions Read the following sentences. Underline each word that has a hard-**g** sound, and circle each word that has a soft-**g** sound.

Rule When **g** is followed by **e, i,** or **y,** the **g** is usually soft. Soft **g** stands for the /j/ sound as in urge.

1. The theater group is presenting a magic show again this weekend.

2. A large, energetic cast will be on the stage.

3. This group has been rehearsing great tricks and grand stunts.

4. Tom, a talented magician, will appear in a green and orange turban.

5. The audience will never guess how he makes birds appear in an empty cage!

Name _____

groups	college	cement	great
circle	badge	gold	cool
huge	center	cases	guests

1. Mr. Rosen's class went on a trip to a _____ campus.

2. It was a _____ autumn day, perfect for a brisk walk.

3. Each student wore a _____ with his or her name.

4. The class split into two _____ and toured the campus.

5. The first group walked to the _____ of the small campus.

6. They admired the trees with _____ and red leaves.

7. Mr. Rosen led the second group along a _____ path.

8. They went to the science building, which was shaped like a

   _____.

9. Inside, they studied items in display _____.

10. Carol and Vicki liked the _____ bones.

11. College students called out greetings to their _____.

12. On the way home the class agreed it had been a _____ day.

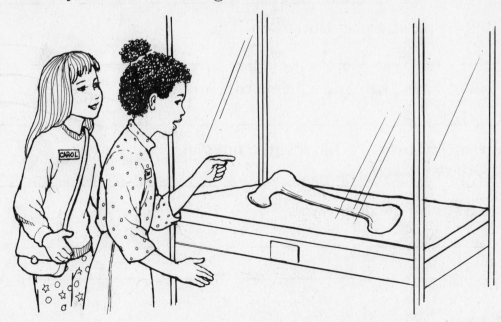

The Cat and the Cookies

Cynthia and Ginny like to cook. One day they decided to make cinnamon cookies and gingerbread for their pals. They used spices including cinnamon and ginger.

Soon the cookies and gingerbread were baked to a golden color. Then Cynthia and Ginny arranged them on a large orange plate. They decorated the cookies with fancy gumdrops. Cynthia covered the cookies and gingerbread. Next she placed them on the window ledge to cool. Then the pals drank some cider.

They decided to go to the garage to fix Ginny's ten-speed bicycle. Later they would have the cinnamon cookies and a slice of gingerbread.

Before long Ginny heard her mother calling. Then she saw Cinderella, her cat, running behind the garage. At once she guessed what had occurred because Cinderella had traces of gumdrops all over her face. Ginny wasn't angry since she cared a lot for Cinderella. They all agreed that Cinderella looked comical!

1. Where were the cookies and gingerbread placed to cool?

_____

2. What word describes the bits of gumdrop on Cinderella's face?

_____

3. What two kinds of spices did you read about?

_____

4. What did the pals have to drink?

_____

5. What word names the place where a car can be kept?

_____

6. Find a word in the story that means "not plain."

_____

7. What had Cinderella done?

_____

_____

LESSON 8: Test: Hard and soft C and G

Name _____

Definition A **consonant blend** is two or more consonants sounded together so that each sound is heard.

EXAMPLES

black   **tr**ain   **spr**ing

Directions Say the name of each picture. Circle the blend you hear at the beginning of each picture's name.

1. 	bl fl pl sl	**2.** 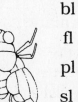	fr tr gr pr

3.   dr cr br tr   **4.** cl fl gl sl

5.  gr cr br tr   **6.** 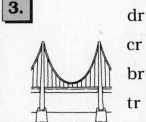 pl cl bl fl   **7.**  gr dr br tr   **8.** 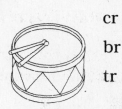 dr cr br tr

Directions Circle the word that completes each sentence, and write it on the line.

1. The little bridge was made of wooden _____.

        planks
        clanks
        plates

2. We crossed the bridge and walked along the _____.

        frail
        train
        trail

3. We soon came upon a small, _____ cottage.

        true
        glue
        blue

LESSON 9: R and L blends

1. flat

fla____ (to wave)

fl____p (to turn over)

fl____p (to fall)

2. slip

sl____p (to hit)

sla____ (to close)

sl____m (thin)

3. brick

____rick (to fool)

tr____ck (a path)

____rack (to break)

4. trade

____rade (a test mark)

gra____e (a kind of fruit)

____rape (a curtain)

5. clank

____lank (a board)

plan____ (a jet)

pla____e (to put)

6. trim

tri____ (a journey)

tr____p (to catch)

tra____ (a kind of train)

Directions Complete each sentence with a word you wrote above.

1. The girls take a _____ to their clubhouse.

2. They pack a snack of fruit and _____ drink.

3. They _____ the boys by sneaking out the door.

4. Jo takes along a wooden _____.

5. The plank has just one small _____.

6. Suki will carefully _____ the board in the doorway.

7. The new door looks better than the old _____.

8. It is too sturdy to _____ in the breeze.

9. The girls _____ down in the grass to rest.

Name _____

Directions Say the name of each picture. Circle the blend you hear at the beginning of each picture's name.

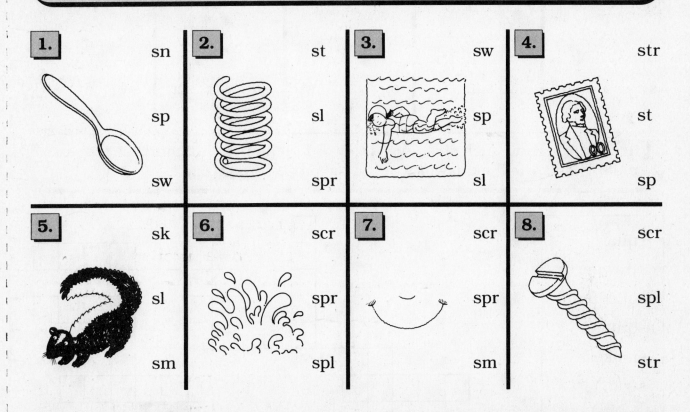

1.	sn	2.	st	3.	sw	4.	str
	sp		sl		sp		st
	sw		spr		sl		sp
5.	sk	6.	scr	7.	scr	8.	scr
	sl		spr		spr		spl
	sm		spl		sm		str

Directions Complete each sentence with a word from the box.

sleet	skid	stream	snug
storm	slip	sway	scarves

1. A severe ice _____ has struck the city.

2. Traffic does not flow in its usual _____.

3. Instead, cars _____ on the icy streets.

4. The high winds cause cars to _____.

5. People _____ and fall on the ice.

6. They are dressed warmly in hats and _____.

7. They wish they were _____ in their homes.

8. The forecast calls for additional _____!

19

LESSON 10: S blends

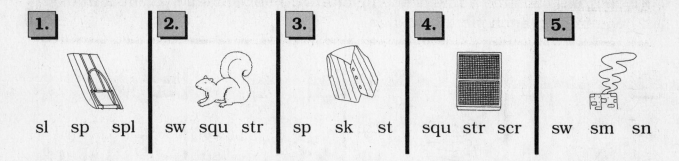

1. sl   sp   spl

2. sw   squ   str

3. sp   sk   st

4. squ   str   scr

5. sw   sm   sn

Directions Read each clue. Find the word in the box that matches the clue. Then write the answer word in the crossword puzzle.

square
strawberry
squeezed
squirrel
smoke
strip
splash
split
slice
smell
strap
sled
squad

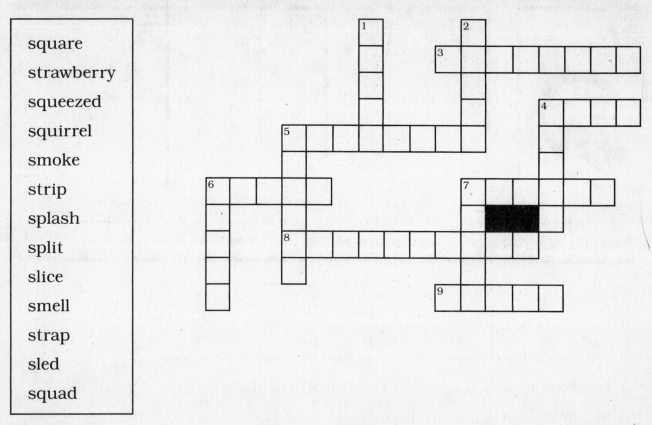

Across

3. a small animal with a long bushy tail
4. used for sliding on the snow
5. pressed or forced together
6. an odor or a scent
7. a flat figure with four equal sides
8. a small, red, juicy fruit
9. to separate into two parts

Down

1. gas and bits of carbon that rise from something burning
2. a small group of football players
4. a narrow strip of leather
5. to make a liquid scatter and fall in drops
6. to cut with a knife
7. a long narrow piece of land or material

Name _____

Directions Say the name of the picture. Write the letters that correctly complete each word.

1. _____ing

2. _____agon

3. _____ant

4. _____ing

5. _____ash

6. _____ain

7. _____eet

8. _____ew

9. _____ide

10. _____obe

Directions Complete the unfinished word in each sentence with the correct blend.

1. Two police officers came to our school to ___ ___eak. (st, sp, cr)

2. They discussed bicycle safety with the entire ___ ___ass. (cr, gl, cl)

3. Officer Jones went to ___ ___and in front of the room. (st, gl, str)

4. He quickly ___ ___anced toward the back of the room. (gl, st, spl)

5. In back, Officer Wilson was ___ ___eering a bicycle. (st, cl, gl)

6. She taught the class to follow ___ ___oper safety habits. (gr, cr, pr)

7. We discussed the way to cross the ___ ___ ___eet. (chr, str, shr)

8. Officer Jones ___ ___oudly displayed a safety helmet. (cr, pr, gr)

9. The officers wanted the ___ ___oup to ask questions. (dr, sc, gr)

10. They were ___ ___eased with our response. (pr, gl, pl)

Hint Some words end with a consonant blend.

EXAMPLES
de**nt**   fa**st**   la**mp**   ma**sk**
ha**nd**   dri**nk**   wa**sp**

Directions Circle the word in each pair in which you hear a final blend.

1. tin – tint   2. wink – win   3. kind – kit   4. risk – rise
5. cat – cast   6. wan – want   7. think – thin   8. cramp – cram
9. hunt – hut   10. chump – chum   11. mat – mast   12. bend – Ben
13. ramp – ram   14. base – bask   15. pain – paint   16. toad – toast
17. ten – tend   18. bun – bunt   19. on – bond   20. bad – band

Directions Read each definition. Then write the word from the list that goes with it. Circle the blends in the words you write.

Hint The meaning of a word is its definition.

plank	mask	print	sink	stump	rent
task	limp	coast	vest	blend	

1. a basin in the kitchen that has a drain and water faucets _____

2. a kind of jacket without sleeves _____

3. part of the tree left after it has been cut down _____

4. edge of land facing the sea _____

5. walk in a lame way _____

6. to mix together _____

7. the kind of mark often made by a foot or finger _____

8. face covering with openings for the eyes _____

9. a long, wide, thick board _____

10. money paid for the use of an apartment _____

11. work that one must do _____

LESSON 11: Final blends

Name _____

Directions Read the story and answer the questions. Then underline each word in the story that begins with a consonant blend.

The Different Drummer

Brad Brown and his friends like music. All of them play instruments. One spring afternoon, Brad and five others decided to start a band. Glenda played the French horn, and Stan played the tuba. Flossy and Scott each played the trombone. Brad played the trumpet. Brenda, Brad's twin sister, played the clarinet. The only problem was that the band had no drummer. They decided to play anyway.

Brad placed seats for the band near some spruce trees in the driveway. The band's first number was "Twilight on the Trail." Music filled the air. The tuba glittered in the sunlight. The trombones sparkled. The French horn twinkled. The pleasing sounds woke Scottie, Brad's dog, who had been snoozing by the house.

Suddenly the band began to hear strange sounds. Tramp, bang, rum, trum, drum! Scottie had hopped onto an old wooden tub that was upside down. Tramp, bang, rum, trum, drum!

"Scram, Scottie!" pleaded Brad.

Scottie would *not* scram. Tramp, bang, rum, trum, drum!

"Well, folks," claimed Brad. "Whether we like it or not, we have a drummer!"

So the band played on, this time with its frisky new drummer.

1. Brad's dog was snoozing. Write another word for snoozing. The word you write should begin with the same blend as the name of this picture.

    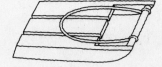

    _____

2. Find three words in the story that begin with the same blend as the name of this picture.

    _____ _____

3. Find five words in the story that begin with the same blend as the name of this picture.

    _____ _____ _____ _____

Directions Complete each sentence by writing a word from the box.

sky	cried	dragged	planet	stars
clapped	twilight	squeal	cloudy	

1. At _____, we set up the telescope.

2. We _____ it to the front lawn.

3. The _____ were just appearing.

4. We looked up in the night _____.

5. Todd let out a _____ of delight.

6. He _____ his hands in excitement.

7. "I see it! I see it!" he _____.

8. "I'm sure I see the _____ Mars."

9. Soon the sky became _____.

Directions Complete the unfinished word in each sentence with the correct blend.

sp	str	gl	spl	st
sq	scr	tr	sk	

1. The Greens look at their family ___ ___ ___apbook.

2. Here is a picture of Amy at her de___ ___.

3. Kevin sees a picture from a ski ___ ___ip.

4. In the picture, he is wearing heavy ___ ___oves.

5. Another picture shows Mom making a roa___ ___.

6. Here is a nice shot of Dad in a ___ ___ ___iped tie.

7. Amy has a photo of her cheerleading ___ ___uad.

8. All the cheerleaders are doing ___ ___ ___its.

9. The Greens treasure these ___ ___ ecial photos.

24

LESSON 12: Test: Blends

Name _____

Definition A **consonant digraph** is two consonants that together represent one sound.	**EXAMPLES**

Digraph	Beginning	Middle	Ending
sh	**sh**ip	a**sh**es	fi**sh**
th	**th**ing	mo**th**er	tee**th**
ch	**ch**icks	ex**ch**ange	ri**ch**
wh	**wh**en	a**wh**ile	—

Directions Circle two pictures in each row whose names contain the consonant digraph sound you hear in the first word.

1. brush

2. thirty

3. wheat

Directions Circle the word that correctly completes each sentence, and write it on the line.

1. Mr. Batt is _____ of the football team. (cough, coach)

2. He wears a shiny _____ around his neck. (thistle, whistle)

3. The players will _____ the ball. (throw, chow)

4. The boys _____ equipment onto the field. (wheel, wreath)

5. Mr. Batt warns them about a _____ of mud. (patch, peach)

6. Everyone wears large _____ pads. (shudder, shoulder)

LESSON 13: Consonant digraphs SH, TH, WH, CH

Directions Underline each word that has the consonant digraph **sh, ch, th,** or **wh.** Then circle each digraph.

1. chain
2. whale
3. teacher
4. tablet
5. wheat
6. woman
7. shelf
8. shore
9. sheep
10. walnut
11. season
12. thorn
13. winter
14. tanker
15. thin
16. peach
17. wheel
18. thimble
19. kitchen
20. chick

Definition An **analogy** describes the relationship one thing has to another.

Example
Car is to **road** as **boat** is to **water.**

Directions Read each sentence. Think about the way the first two words are related. Then choose one of the words you underlined above to complete the sentence.

1. **Seed** is to **apple** as **pit** is to _____peach_____.
2. **Forest** is to **woods** as **beach** is to _____.
3. **Lion** is to **jungle** as _____ is to **sea.**
4. **Banana** is to **fruit** as _____ is to **grain.**
5. **Blade** is to **skate** as _____ is to **truck.**
6. **Ring** is to **finger** as _____ is to **neck.**
7. **Cow** is to **calf** as **hen** is to _____.
8. **Wolves** are to **pack** as _____ are to **flock.**
9. **Quill** is to **porcupine** as _____ is to **rose.**
10. **Car** is to **garage** as **stove** is to _____.
11. **Hammer** is to **carpentry** as _____ is to **sewing.**
12. **Plump** is to **chubby** as **lean** is to _____.
13. **Sing** is to **singer** as **teach** is to _____.
14. **Clothes** are to **closet** as **books** are to _____.

LESSON 13: Consonant digraphs SH, TH, WH, CH

Name _____

Rule Usually **ch** stands for the sound you hear at the beginning and end of church. Sometimes **ch** can stand for the /sh/ sound or the /k/ sound.

EXAMPLES

chipmunk   **ch**ef   **ch**orus
or**ch**ard   **ch**ip   **ch**emist

1. Mr. Christy took our school choir and orchestra on a field trip.
2. We went to a restaurant called the Chic Steakhouse.
3. Pictures of cartoon characters were on the walls.
4. A large, bright chandelier hung from the ceiling.
5. Every table had a vase of fresh chrysanthemums.
6. The chef, Charlene, made delicious chicken.
7. Our waitress, Charlotte, served us with a smile.
8. The lemon chiffon pie was their specialty.
9. I had grapes and cherries for dessert.
10. At the end of the meal, our teacher paid the check.
11. We left our extra change and cheered our waitress.

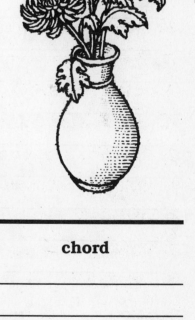

church	chef	chord
_____	_____	_____
_____	_____	_____
_____	_____	_____
_____	_____	_____
_____	_____	_____
_____	_____	_____

Directions Read each word in the box and circle its consonant digraph. Then write the word in the correct column according to the position of the consonant digraph.

wharf	spinach	shoulder	cheap	switch	cheese
porch	whale	orchid	mushroom	teeth	dishes
merchant	relish	architect	orchestra	teacher	thin
arch	chemist	shutters	lunchtime	path	crush
ditch	chorus	brother	urchin	think	bunch
mother	whip	leash	moth	chaperon	pitcher

Beginning

_____
_____
_____
_____
_____
_____
_____
_____
_____
_____
_____
_____

Middle

_____
_____
_____
_____
_____
_____
_____
_____
_____
_____
_____
_____

End

_____
_____
_____
_____
_____
_____
_____
_____
_____
_____
_____
_____

LESSON 14: Consonant digraphs SH, TH, WH, CH

Name _____

Wonderful Workers

Chris and Sherry spent part of their school vacation doing errands and odd jobs in their neighborhood. Through their hard work, they hoped to earn enough money to spend a month at a theater camp.

Chris's dad hired them to sand and paint some shutters. He was so happy with their work that he paid them to stain the front porch a beautiful chocolate brown. The girls then chose to use some of their earnings to place an ad in a local newspaper. The day after the ad appeared, the phone began ringing with job offers.

One week the girls did yard chores for Mrs. Sheer. They gathered up branches that had fallen from the trees in the orchard. Then they pulled weeds and raked leaves that were clogging the drainage ditches and covering the flagstone paths. Mrs. Sheer taught them how to prune her chrysanthemum plants and some beautiful wild forsythia bushes.

Before they realized it, the girls had earned enough money for their stay at camp. When Sherry's mother met the camp chaperon, she said, "These girls pitched in and earned most of the cash they needed for camp. If they work as hard at acting as they do at household chores, they'll be stars for sure!"

1. What kind of camp did Sherry and Chris want to attend? _____

_____

2. What two jobs did Chris's dad hire the girls to do? _____

_____

3. What kind of work did the girls do for Mrs. Sheer? _____

_____

4. What word in the story means "area of land on which fruit trees are

grown"? _____

5. What kinds of flowering plants did the girls learn to care for? _____

_____

1. The city is hosting a gymnastics ___ ___ow.

2. The show's ___ ___eme this year is "Jumping for Joy."

3. The city ___ ___oral group sings the show's theme song.

4. Patrick runs on stage and turns four cart___ ___eels.

5. The audience claps and ___ ___istles at his skills.

6. Brittany presents a ___ ___allenging floor routine.

7. From the crowd, her brothers ___ ___eer loudly.

8. The ___ ___orus presents another number.

9. Some people clap along to the rhy___ ___m of the music.

10. The stagehand pu___ ___es a balance beam onto the floor.

11. Rose exercises ___ ___ile she waits backstage.

12. She stret___ ___es her muscles to avoid injury.

13. When they call her name, she da___ ___es out to center stage.

14. The audience is ___ ___rilled by her graceful routine.

15. Jason and Phil come on stage, ___ ___en Rose exits.

16. They wear matching ___ ___ite and blue costumes.

17. They rub their hands in ___ ___alk before their routine.

18. Jason ___ ___ispers, "Good luck, Phil!"

Name _____

		Vowels					Vowels	
		Seen	Heard				Seen	Heard
1.	frame	2	1	17.	wild		____	____
2.	cabin	____	____	18.	animal		____	____
3.	coat	____	____	19.	struck		____	____
4.	deep	____	____	20.	butterfly		____	____
5.	cannot	____	____	21.	office		____	____
6.	beat	____	____	22.	children		____	____
7.	hotel	____	____	23.	sleeve		____	____
8.	feel	____	____	24.	sentence		____	____
9.	stain	____	____	25.	Steve		____	____
10.	funny	____	____	26.	music		____	____
11.	visit	____	____	27.	Thanksgiving		____	____
12.	rich	____	____	28.	roasted		____	____
13.	stand	____	____	29.	gently		____	____
14.	read	____	____	30.	cathedral		____	____
15.	basket	____	____	31.	something		____	____
16.	weed	____	____	32.	colt		____	____

Hint If you hear one vowel sound in a word, the word has one syllable. If you hear two vowel sounds in a word, the word has two syllables, and so on.

gymnast	cage	whale	gingerbread	trace	children
desk	giraffe	radio	wild	splashing	guest
agent	understand	celery	garden	decide	including
happiness	fence	consonant	pencil	grocery	post

One Syllable	Two Syllables	Three Syllables

Directions Here are some titles of songs you may know. Circle each two-syllable word and underline each word with three syllables.

1. "Old McDonald Had a Farm"
2. "The Bluebird of Happiness"
3. "The Battle Hymn of the Republic"
4. "America the Beautiful"
5. "Twinkle, Twinkle Little Star"

Name _____

Directions Say the name of each picture. Listen for the **ar** sound as in *farm*. If you hear the sound, write the picture name on the line and circle the **ar**.

Rule The letters **ar** can stand for the vowel sound you hear in *farm*.

1. _____

2. _____

3. _____

4. _____

5. _____

6. _____

7. _____

8. _____

Directions Complete each sentence with a word from the box.

1. We read a story about Tony, a castle _____.

2. The best _____ described his job.

3. Tony _____ in front of the castle each day.

4. He made sure the doorknocker _____.

5. He rolled out the king's red _____.

6. He helped the king into his royal _____.

7. Tony responded when _____ rang.

8. He stopped visitors with a wave of his _____.

9. He even tended the royal flower _____.

10. Tony never believed his job was _____.

sparkled
alarms
guard
carpet
hard
arm
cart
marched
garden
part

Rule The letters **ar** can stand for different vowel sounds. In some words these letters follow Long-Vowel Rule 1: If a syllable has two vowels, the first vowel usually stands for the long sound and the second is silent.

EXAMPLES

c**ar**e   d**ar**e   sh**ar**e

r**ar**e   h**ar**e   sp**ar**e

Directions Read the words in the box. Then write a word from the box to answer each question. Each word you write must contain **ar** and follow Long-Vowel Rule 1.

foal	box	flares	pare
dead	dimestore	flashlights	slice
square	mare	hardware	bare

1. What shape has four sides? _____

2. What do police officers often light at the scene of an accident? _____

3. What can you do to an apple to remove its skin? _____

4. In what kind of store can you find tools? _____

5. What is a female horse called? _____

6. What do you call a tree without leaves? _____

Directions Circle three words in each row that have the same vowel sound.

1. bark   hare   market   far

2. yard   spare   beware   rare

3. harm   guard   stare   yarn

4. partner   spark   garment   care

LESSON 17: AR words

Name _____

Directions Say the name of each picture. Listen for the **or** sound as in **corn.** If you hear the sound, write the picture name on the line and circle the **or.**

Rule The letters **or** can stand for the vowel sound you hear in corn.

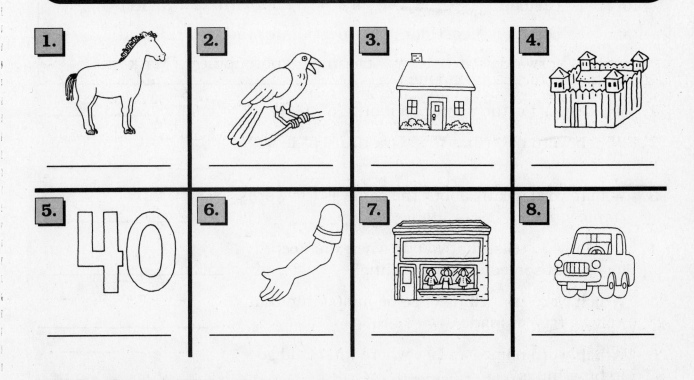

1. _____

2. _____

3. _____

4. _____

5. _____

6. _____

7. _____

8. _____

Directions Complete each sentence with a word from the box.

1. This _____, we took a walk.

2. We started at the _____ end of town.

3. We passed many small _____.

4. At the _____ in the road, we turned.

5. We traveled past an old _____.

6. It is a famous _____ landmark.

7. A _____ always burns in front of it.

8. We saw the hospital in which I was _____.

9. A crowd had gathered at a street _____.

10. They watched a musician playing a _____.

| corner |
| horn |
| morning |
| fort |
| torch |
| north |
| historical |
| born |
| fork |
| stores |

Directions Read each question. Find the answer in the box, and write the word on the line.

sport	organ	charcoal	March	army	marshmallow
story	cartoon	spare	rare	orchard	share
stare	corner	corridor	carpet	tornado	orchid
market	forward	artist	parsnip	porcupine	Mark

1. Which word is the name of a month of the year? _____

2. Which word describes the extra tire kept in a car? _____

3. Which word means about the same as the words *comic strip*? _____

4. Which word tells what you do when you keep looking at someone or something? _____

5. Which word is a telling of some happening that may be true or made up? _____

6. Which word names a place where you could go to buy things? _____

7. Which word is a person who paints or draws very well? _____

8. Which word names something white, sticky, and sweet? _____

9. Which word is a fuel you might use when cooking hot dogs on a grill? _____

10. Which word names an animal that has stiff, sharp spines? _____

11. Which word is a piece of land where fruit trees grow? _____

12. Which word is a name for a hallway or passageway? _____

13. Which word describes something that is unusual and seldom found? _____

LESSON 18: AR and OR words

Name _____

1.

near
north
nurse
first

2.

fern
arm
form
firm

3.

thirsty
thrifty
thirty
thirteen

4.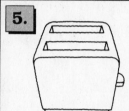

circle
circus
city
cider

5.

toaster
roaster
topper
ticket

6.

turkey
tricky
trip
turnip

Directions Complete each sentence with a word from the box.

1. Next _____ is a special day for the Dodd family.

2. The twins, Mike and May, will celebrate their

   _____.

3. They will be _____ years old on that day.

4. Mrs. Dodd will prepare their favorite _____.

5. She will prepare a delicious roasted _____.

6. Mr. Dodd will make his famous apple

   _____.

7. The twins' favorite vegetables are peas and

   _____.

8. Their _____ promises to prepare both.

9. After dinner, the family will go to the

   _____.

| birthday |
| dinner |
| cider |
| turnips |
| circus |
| Thursday |
| thirteen |
| turkey |
| mother |

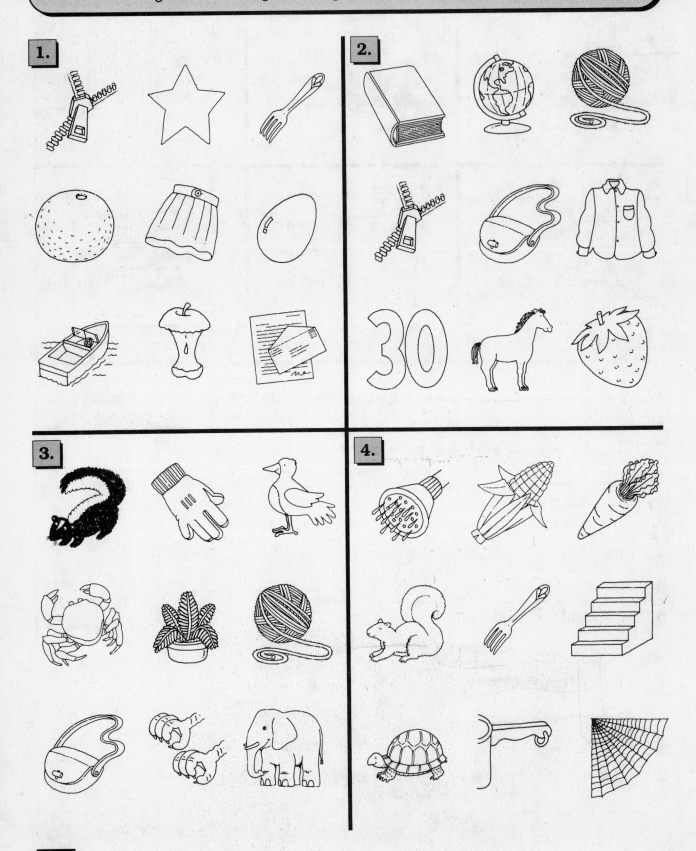

Name _____

Directions Complete each sentence with a word from the box.

1. Williamsburg is a colonial town in

   _____.

2. The town, its streets, and its homes are

   _____.

3. An old _____ stands as it was in the past.

4. Craftspeople make colonial _____.

5. A woman _____ wax as she makes candles.

6. The candles are red and _____.

7. Other people, in colonial costumes,

   _____ butter.

8. Restaurants _____ traditional colonial meals.

9. _____ in American history conduct tours.

10. Street dancers _____ past the curious crowds.

11. In a barn, a cow is fed _____ of corn.

12. The _____ Mansion is a popular attraction.

13. Smoke _____ from its huge brick chimney.

Virginia
furniture
kernels
curls
Governor's
whirl
preserved
church
stirs
Experts
serve
churn
purple

Rule In some words, the letters **er, ir, or, ur** follow Long-Vowel Rule 1: If a syllable has two vowels, the first vowel usually stands for the long sound and the second is silent.

h**er**e   f**ir**e
c**or**e   p**ur**e

Directions Read each word. Circle each word in which **er, ir, or,** or **ur** follows Long-Vowel Rule 1.

1. snore	2. cures	3. work	4. firm	5. floor
6. thirty	7. burr	8. core	9. hire	10. worm
11. severe	12. score	13. door	14. purr	15. retire
16. spire	17. lure	18. more	19. tires	20. store

Directions Read each clue. Find the word you circled above which matches the clue. Then write the answer word in the crossword puzzle.

Across
2. these are found on a car or bike
5. greater in number
7. part of a church
8. attract with bait
9. opening in a wall
11. to pay someone to do a job
12. sound made while sleeping
13. the part of a room to walk on

Down
1. center of an apple
3. teams' points
4. strict or harsh
6. a doctor helps find these
7. a place of business where things are bought and sold
10. give up a job

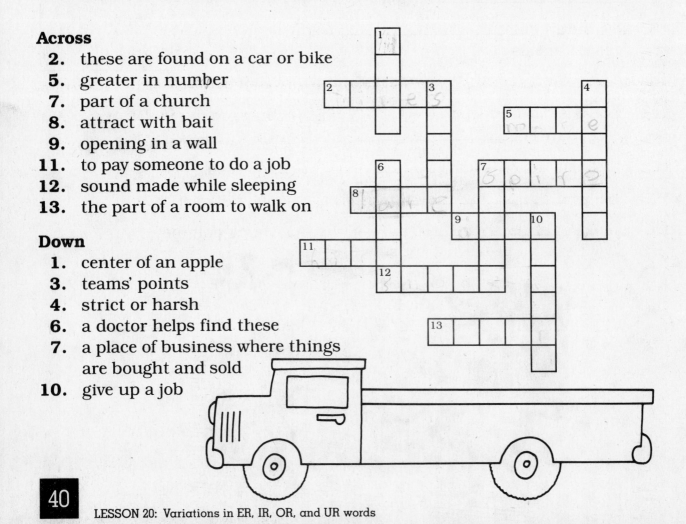

LESSON 20: Variations in ER, IR, OR, and UR words

Name _____

Directions Read the sentence in each box and draw a picture of it. Be sure your picture clearly shows what the sentence means. Then circle the words in each sentence that contain **ar, or, er, ir,** or **ur.**

1. Nervous Barbara hopes to survive her daring ride on the Ferris wheel.

2. During a storm, a horrible monster, attired in a scarlet cloak, surprises a scared person.

3. Serious Mort can ride bareback, play the harmonica, and twirl a derby, all at the same time.

4. Charming Clare has a purple uniform and serves as a stern umpire.

1.   **farm**

While playing in the yard near the marsh, Scott fell.

He felt a sharp pain in his arm as he tried to get up.

From the park, Mr. Dark saw Scott fall and ran to help.

Scott's friend, Mark, also came to lend a hand.

Fortunately, the fall did not do Scott much harm.

2.   **corn**

With a blast, the horn sounded an alarm to the town.

A tornado of incredible force was approaching quickly.

People living near the port quickly took shelter.

Some doors blew open, but there was little damage.

In no more than five minutes, the tornado had passed.

3.   **here**

Looking for deer, Josie walked quietly in the woods.

Steering clear of noisy picnickers, she moved ahead.

She thought she could hear something moving.

Looking up, she saw a small doe near the trees.

The tiny animal showed no fear of Josie.

4.   **tire**

Mrs. Nelson owns the inn with the tall spires.

Visitors admire the lovely inn and its sprawling lawn.

Mrs. Nelson is planning to hire someone to assist her.

Just lighting a fire in each room takes her hours!

5.   **burn**

Don has just returned from the hospital.

He was at Central City Hospital for surgery.

Don arrived at the hospital on Thursday morning.

While waiting for his turn, he joked with a nurse.

LESSON 21: Test: Vowel + R words

Name _____

Directions Say the name of each picture and listen for the /k/ sound. Fill in the first, middle, or last box to show whether the sound of **k** comes at the beginning, middle, or end of the word.

1. □ □ □

2. □ □ □

3. □ □ □

4. □ □ □

5. □ □ □

6. □ □ □

7. □ □ □

8. □ □ □

9. □ □ □

10. □ □ □

11. □ □ □

12. □ □ □

13. □ □ □

14. □ □ □

15. □ □ □

16. □ □ □

17. □ □ □

18. □ □ □

19. □ □ □

20. □ □ □

LESSON 22: Words that contain the K sound

Rule The letters **k** and **ck** stand for the /k/ sound. The letter **c** stands for the /k/ sound if it comes before the letters **a**, **o**, or **u**.

EXAMPLES

kitten   pi**ck**
can   **c**ost

Directions Complete each sentence by writing a word from the parentheses that has the /k/ sound. Then circle the letter or letters that stand for the/k/ sound.

1. The girls' soccer team is _____ plans for a fundraiser. (arranging, making)

2. Ms. Garcia, their _____, is helping. (coach, sponsor)

3. Jennie, the team _____, is taking notes. (leader, captain)

4. She _____ notes as the girls give suggestions. (takes, writes)

5. Later, Jennie _____ her notes. (copies, more)

6. The team uses them to _____ the best idea. (choose, pick)

7. The team votes to hold a _____ sale. (bake, pie)

8. Nicki and Laura will make _____ to sell. (cheese, cookies)

9. Loni will prepare _____ whipped cream pies. (rich, thick)

10. Peg will operate the _____ register. (cash, change)

11. Everyone will make _____ posters to hang. (bright, colored)

12. The sale will be advertised in the _____ papers. (town, local)

13. It will be held in the _____ near the school. (park, yard)

14. The team will set up a huge _____ there. (canopy, tent)

44

LESSON 22: Words with the K sound

Name _____

Rule The letters **ch** can stand for the /k/ sound as in *school* or the /ch/ sound as in *church*. The letters **que** can also stand for the /k/ sound as in *technique*.

EXAMPLES

a**ch**e   ea**ch**   uni**que**

Directions Circle each word in which you see **ch**. Then write each word in the correct column.

1. Twenty children were chosen to attend a school assembly.
2. Each one sits in a chair in front of a chalkboard.
3. The schedule shows the order of the speakers on a chart.
4. An architect who designs kitchens goes first.
5. An orchestra leader and a choral director speak next.
6. A chemist, a mechanic, and a chemistry teacher speak last.

ch as in **ache** | **ch** as in **each**

_____ _____ | _____ _____

_____ _____ | _____ _____

_____ _____ | _____ _____

_____ _____ | _____ _____

Directions Complete each sentence with a word from the box at the right.

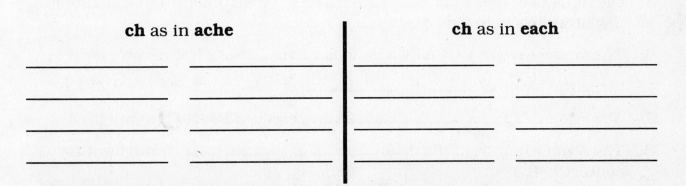

1. We searched through the _____ shop.
2. We found many old and unusual, or _____, items.
3. Some were made with _____ seldom used today.
4. I have never seen one _____ item in the shop!

| unique ✓ |
| techniques |
| grotesque ✓ |
| antique ✓ |

Rule The letters **qu** stand for the /kw/ sound.

EXAMPLES

quote   **qu**ick   **qu**ilt

Directions Complete each sentence with a word from the box.

quiet	conductor	keys	plucked
echoed	unique	piccolo	orchestra

1. My dad took me to listen to a famous _____ from Russia.

2. As the lights dimmed, the audience became very _____.

3. Everyone applauded when the orchestra's _____ walked onto the stage.

4. I enjoyed watching the violinists as they _____ the strings on their violins.

5. One musician had a _____ instrument that was unlike any other in the world.

6. The orchestra was joined by a famous pianist whose fingers breezed along the piano _____.

7. The silver _____ shimmered under the bright lights.

8. The strong sounds of the drum _____ throughout the concert hall.

LESSON 23: Words with the QU and K sound

Name _____

Rule The letters **ph** and **gh** can stand for the /f/ sound.

EXAMPLES

dol**ph**in   lau**gh**

Directions Say each word. Underline the letters that stand for the /f/ sound. Then write the words under the correct headings.

phones	photo	feature	triumph	orphan
fingers	telephone	rough	typhoid	enough
cough	telegraph	typhoon	phonics	Philip
graph	furniture	finish	sulphur	fine
feathers	phony	digraph	fail	pamphlet
	tough	laugh	nephew	

(ph)

_____ _____ _____ _____

_____ _____ _____ _____

_____ _____ _____ _____

_____ _____ _____ _____

(gh)

_____ _____ _____ _____

(f)

_____ _____ _____ _____

Directions Read the poem below. Underline each word in the story that has the sound of **f**. Then circle the word that completes each sentence and write the word on the line.

The Fantastic Frog

A frog in a city, it just can't be true.

It must be a phantom or a statue,

A dolphin perhaps, or elephant maybe,

But how could a frog in the city be happy?

But look! There is Philip, in his suit and tie,

Looking quite smart and not a bit shy.

Reading the papers is one of his crazes,

Finding the meaning from paragraphs and phrases.

He uses the phone like a city tycoon

And rushes around like a wild typhoon,

Shopping in big stores and riding in autos,

Watching the people and taking some photos.

When asked why he left his home in the pool,

He laughed as he said, "Well, I'm not a fool.

The water was wet and the going was rough.

To tell you quite frankly, I'd had quite enough."

His biography will be read with amazement,

For a frog out of water—that's quite an achievement!

1. Philip was a _____.   (elephant, dolphin, frog)

2. He rushes around like a

    _____.   (phantom, hyphen, typhoon)

3. When asked why he left the pool,

    Philip _____.   (laughed, coughed, phoned)

4. His _____ will be   (pamphlet, biography, phonograph)
    read with amazement.

Name _____

<table>
<tr><td>Rule The letter s can stand for the /s/, /z/, or /sh/ sounds.</td><td>EXAMPLES

    safe   rose   sure</td></tr>
</table>

Directions Read the sentences below and underline all the words that have the letter **s**. Then write each underlined word in the correct column.

1. Surely you will attend the piano recital on Tuesday.

2. Let me assure you that you will enjoy our program.

3. Don't think I'm pressuring you to attend it, though!

4. A large audience will assemble to observe us.

5. I'm certain that their applause will be reassuring.

6. We will present a long list of classical music.

7. Several people will also play popular tunes.

8. I can ensure that you will have a good time!

9. We will be delighted to pose for pictures with you.

10. We will give everyone an issue of our piano program.

11. I will play "The Sugar Song" and another number.

12. They will be quite moving, so bring plenty of tissue!

s as in **safe**	**s** as in **rose**	**s** as in **sure**

LESSON 25: The sounds S can stand for

1. We rose early on the farm.

2. After rising, we ate breakfast.

3. Andy served oatmeal with sugar.

4. Then we began our chores.

5. Sam raked the fallen leaves.

6. Cousin Rosie fed the cows.

7. Esther pruned the roses.

8. The morning surely flew!

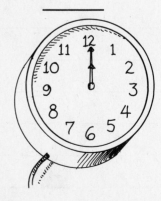

Name _____

Directions Read the sentence in each box and draw a picture of it. Then circle the words in each sentence that have a silent **gh**.

Hint Sometimes **gh** is silent and does not have any sound.

1. Our neighbor's daughter ought to be taught to fight pollution.

2. They sought the naughty cat and found him in the bough of a mighty tree.

3. We sighed when we learned that our flight had left and was flying high.

4. We weighed the dough and made eight pizzas right there.

Rule The letters **rh** stand for the /r/ sound. The **h** is silent.

EXAMPLES

rhythm   **rh**inoceros

Directions   Complete each sentence with a word from the box.

| Rhode Island   rhymes   rhubarb   rhododendron |

1. Tara loves to visit her grandmother in _____.

2. She and Tara work outside, tending the _____ bushes.

3. As they work, they make up silly _____ and laugh.

4. In the cool evenings, they make _____ pies.

Rule The letters **wr** stand for the /r/ sound. The **w** is silent.

EXAMPLES

wrong   **wr**ing

Directions   Complete each sentence with a word from the box.

| wrong   wrist   wrestle   wrap |

1. The boys are learning to _____ in gym class.

2. The coach cautions against using the _____ holds.

3. Moving incorrectly could result in an injured _____.

4. Some boys _____ their knees for extra support.

LESSON 26: Silent letters in RH, WR words

Name _____

Rule The letters **gn** or **kn** stand for the /n/ sound. The **g** and the **k** are silent.

EXAMPLES

gnaw   **kn**ew

Directions Complete each sentence with a word from the box.

1. Lance, a brave _____, lives in a forest.

2. The forest is filled with _____ trees.

3. Legend says that a _____ lives in one tree.

4. This creature is no taller than your _____.

5. He dresses in baggy _____ and a red vest.

6. Lance is anxious to get to _____ this elf.

7. Searching, Lance peeks in trees' _____.

gnarled

know

knotholes

knickers

gnome

knee

knight

Rule The letters **sc** or **st** will sometimes stand for the /s/ sound. The **c** and **t** are silent.

EXAMPLES

scene   li**st**en

Directions Complete each sentence with a word from the box.

1. The thief escaped into the _____ village.

2. The police _____ to inform the villagers.

3. With a sharp _____, dogs were called.

4. The dogs picked up the _____ of the thief.

5. With _____ flexed, the dogs ran off.

6. Later, handcuffs _____ on the thief's wrist.

glistened

hastened

scenic

scent

muscles

whistle

LESSON 27: Silent letters in GN, KN, SC, ST words

Directions Complete each sentence with a word from the box.

scent	corrects	antiques	cost	phonograph
coughs	school	photographs	wrong	telephone
writes	laughing	customers	etiquette	orchids

1. After _____, Phil works at Rocco's Pizza Parlor.

2. The restaurant is decorated with unusual _____.

3. Fresh purple _____ are in vases on the tables.

4. Old _____ hang on the walls.

5. An ancient _____ plays lively Italian songs.

6. Phil loves the delicious _____ that greets him at work.

7. Phil is in charge of taking orders over the _____.

8. He always remembers to observe proper phone _____.

9. He never clears his throat or _____ into the phone.

10. As orders are placed, Phil _____ them on order forms.

11. He also informs _____ when their orders will be ready.

12. Then he figures the _____.

13. Sometimes the total is _____.

14. However, he _____ any errors he makes.

15. Phil especially enjoys joking and _____ with patrons.

54

LESSON 27: Review letters that stand for K, F, S sounds; silent letters

Name _____

Directions Read each sentence and find the picture that goes with it. Write the number of the sentence under the picture.

1. The antique camera is placed on a stand.

2. It is clear that the photographer knows the right way to use it.

3. He laughs as he poses people in a scene.

4. His shots are unique and funny.

5. Some subjects dress as knights or physicians. _____

_____   _____   _____   _____

Directions In the sentences above, underline the words in which you hear the /k/ sound, circle the words in which you hear the /f/ sound, and draw a box around the words with silent letters. Then write each word you marked in the correct column.

k sound	f sound	silent letters

55

LESSON 28: Review letters that can stand for K, F, or S sounds; silent letters

Directions Fill in the circle below the word that correctly completes each sentence.

1. Don is learning to use a 35 mm ____.

   camera ○   cough ○   cousin ○

2. He would like to create ____ films.

   critique ○   unique ○   physique ○

3. Don says the camera does not ____ much.

   rough ○   weigh ○   weight ○

4. In fact, he can balance it on his ____.

   knee ○   know ○   knock ○

5. I have asked Don _____ about the camera.

   quick ○   quest ○   questions ○

6. He is always ____ to tell about it.

   clear ○   quick ○   quack ○

7. My ____ and I will appear in Don's film.

   laughed ○   coughed ○   neighbor ○

8. We are ____ the script now.

   writing ○   weight ○   wrote ○

9. We do not yet ____ the title.

   knot ○   know ○   knit ○

10. It will be a scary film about a ____.

    Philip ○   photos ○   phantom ○

11. The film will feature an evil ____.

    chemist ○   choral ○   schedule ○

12. He will work in an ____ laboratory.

    antique ○   unique ○   physique ○

13. A hero will try to keep the town ____.

    sugar ○   safe ○   school ○

14. We will add ____ to the soundtrack.

    rose ○   pose ○   music ○

15. The three of us are ____ it together.

    clothes ○   posing ○   composing ○

16. We are ____ that we will have fun!

    sure ○   sugar ○   silent ○

LESSON 28: Test: Letters that can stand for K, F, or S sounds; silent letters

Name _____

Vowels

		Seen	Heard
1.	furniture	_____	_____
2.	candle	_____	_____
3.	pose	_____	_____
4.	rough	_____	_____
5.	liquid	_____	_____
6.	kite	_____	_____
7.	cough	_____	_____
8.	campaign	_____	_____
9.	cabbage	_____	_____
10.	scientist	_____	_____
11.	quote	_____	_____
12.	gnome	_____	_____
13.	knell	_____	_____
14.	locket	_____	_____
15.	weigh	_____	_____
16.	typhoid	_____	_____

Vowels

		Seen	Heard
17.	enough	_____	_____
18.	gnarl	_____	_____
19.	wrangler	_____	_____
20.	comical	_____	_____
21.	neighbor	_____	_____
22.	insurance	_____	_____
23.	antique	_____	_____
24.	boughs	_____	_____
25.	rhinoceros	_____	_____
26.	cyclone	_____	_____
27.	ache	_____	_____
28.	daughter	_____	_____
29.	chorus	_____	_____
30.	queen	_____	_____
31.	phone	_____	_____
32.	banquet	_____	_____

57

1. jacket _____
2. insect _____
3. glisten _____
4. quiz _____
5. magazine _____
6. mechanic _____
7. Philip _____
8. wrist _____
9. campaign _____
10. cough _____
11. locket _____
12. antique _____
13. rhubarb _____
14. tissue _____
15. wise _____
16. candy _____
17. king _____
18. telephone _____
19. kangaroo _____
20. rhythm _____
21. sign _____
22. wrangler _____
23. gnome _____
24. whisper _____
25. husband _____
26. science _____
27. basement _____
28. rake _____
29. wrong _____
30. phonograph _____
31. rhinoceros _____
32. cousin _____
33. typhoon _____
34. elephant _____
35. phantom _____
36. positive _____
37. wreck _____
38. knapsack _____
39. photo _____
40. kitchen _____
41. chorus _____
42. equal _____
43. block _____
44. digraph _____
45. answer _____
46. sugar _____
47. fight _____
48. inquire _____
49. market _____
50. knoll _____
51. biography _____

LESSON 29: Syllables in words with K, F, or S sounds; silent letters

Name _____

Directions Form new words by adding the suffixes **s**, **ed**, and **ing** to the base words.

Definition The word to which a suffix is added is called **the base word.**

	s	ed	ing
1. work	_____	_____	_____
2. learn	_____	_____	_____
3. cook	_____	_____	_____
4. clean	_____	_____	_____
5. pick	_____	_____	_____
6. help	_____	_____	_____
7. shiver	_____	_____	_____
8. disturb	_____	_____	_____

Directions Write the base word for each word.

1. walks _____	**2.** covered _____
3. guessed _____	**4.** frightens _____
5. talking _____	**6.** lifts _____
7. hitched _____	**8.** cleaned _____
9. buys _____	**10.** picking _____
11. rolling _____	**12.** loves _____
13. packed _____	**14.** burned _____
15. spelling _____	**16.** raining _____

LESSON 30: Suffixes -S, -ED, -ING

Rule When **ed** is added to a base word ending in **d** or **t**, it stands for the **ed** sound in planted. Other times **ed** will stand for the sound of **d** or **t** as in cheered or jumped.

They plant**ed** a tree.
He cheer**ed** for the team.
She jump**ed** over the rope.

Directions Say each word to yourself and listen for the sound **ed** stands for. If the word has the same sound as in **planted**, write **ed** on the line. If the word has a **d** or **t** sound, write **d** or **t** on the line.

1. learned _____
2. called _____
3. heaped _____
4. rushed _____
5. squirted _____
6. carted _____
7. walked _____
8. asked _____
9. shirked _____
10. planted _____
11. fixed _____
12. finished _____
13. served _____
14. turned _____
15. hunted _____

Directions Circle the word that correctly completes each sentence, and write the word on the line.

1. Last summer we _____ to California.

tripped
climbed
traveled

2. We _____ on a warm, sunny morning.

departed
fixed
asked

3. My brother was _____ next to me.

seated
moaned
risked

4. I _____ him if I could sit by the window.

planted
blinked
asked

5. The airplane _____ off smoothly.

loaned
lifted
hatched

LESSON 30: Suffix -ED

Rule The suffix **er** is added to words to compare two things. The suffix **est** is added to words to compare more than two things.

EXAMPLES

My jacket is **warm**.

My coat is **warmer**.

My winter parka is the **warmest** of all.

Directions Read each sentence. Underline each word that is used to compare two things. Circle each word that is used to compare more than two things.

1. This winter went faster than last winter.

2. It is because the weather was nicer.

3. We had the warmest winter in ten years.

4. Temperatures were much higher than usual.

5. Some days were warmer than others.

6. Precipitation was lighter than usual.

7. Last year, the winter wind was stronger.

8. That wind was the wildest I have ever seen.

9. It brought the lowest temperatures ever.

Directions Add the suffixes **er** and **est** to form new words.

		er	est
1.	clear	_____	_____
2.	dark	_____	_____
3.	low	_____	_____
4.	young	_____	_____
5.	short	_____	_____
6.	bright	_____	_____
7.	narrow	_____	_____
8.	smooth	_____	_____

Directions Complete each sentence. Add **er** or **est** to the word in parentheses to make the correct comparative form. Write the new word on the line.

1. We have the _____ class of all! (great)

2. Joe is the _____ runner in the class. (fast)

3. He is even _____ than Rodney. (fast)

4. Pamela gets the _____ grades of all. (high)

5. She has the _____ writing in the class. (neat)

6. I am the _____ student in the school. (tall)

7. Even Mr. Stevens is _____ than I am! (short)

8. Mr. Stevens is _____ than your teacher. (funny)

9. He tells the _____ jokes I've ever heard. (funny)

10. I always laugh the _____ of all. (loud)

Directions Write sentences that tell about the ideas listed below. Use a comparative form in each sentence.

1. the age of two people

Sam is older than Gretchen.

_____

2. the height of three trees

_____

_____

3. the size of two boxes

_____

_____

4. the length of three baseball bats

_____

_____

LESSON 31: Comparative forms -ER, -EST

Name _____

Rule When a word ends in silent **e**, drop the **e** before adding a suffix that begins with a vowel.

EXAMPLES

sav**e** + s = saves
sav**e** + ed = saved
sav**e** + ing = saving

Directions Form new words by adding the correct suffixes. Write the new words on the lines.

	s	**ed**	**ing**
1. pave	_____	_____	_____
2. tease	_____	_____	_____
3. blame	_____	_____	_____
4. describe	_____	_____	_____
5. divide	_____	_____	_____
6. wave	_____	_____	_____

	er	**est**
7. late	_____	_____
8. grave	_____	_____
9. fine	_____	_____
10. cute	_____	_____
11. polite	_____	_____

Directions Write the base word for each word.

1. skating _____ **2.** glides _____

3. traced _____ **4.** hugest _____

5. grazing _____ **6.** later _____

7. nicest _____ **8.** hiking _____

9. icier _____ **10.** rudest _____

LESSON 32: Adding suffixes to words ending in final E

Directions Form a new word by putting each base word and suffix together.

Rule If a word ends in silent **e,** drop the **e** before adding a suffix that begins with a vowel.

1. dive + ing _____
2. wave + ing _____
3. late + est _____
4. love + ed _____
5. smile + ing _____
6. wade + ed _____
7. leave + ing _____
8. come + ing _____
9. cute + est _____
10. face + ing _____

Directions Complete each sentence with one of the new words you formed above.

1. Let's watch the videotape of our _____ day at the beach.

2. Here we are _____ up the walkway.

3. Everyone is smiling and _____ at the camera.

4. Beth really has the _____ smile of all of us!

5. Is this part the _____ contest?

6. This is when Mom _____ with Beth in the shallow water.

7. Here we are getting into the car and _____ for home.

8. We all certainly _____ that day at the beach!

LESSON 32: Adding suffixes to words ending in final E

Name _____

Directions Circle each word that ends in a single consonant. Then add the suffixes to make new words.

Rule When a one-syllable short-vowel word ends in a single consonant, double the consonant before adding a suffix that begins with a vowel.

	ed	**ing**
1. fit	_____	_____
2. act	_____	_____
3. wrap	_____	_____
4. rest	_____	_____
5. blot	_____	_____
6. slip	_____	_____
7. knit	_____	_____

	er	**est**
8. fat	_____	_____
9. fond	_____	_____
10. mad	_____	_____
11. hot	_____	_____
12. cold	_____	_____
13. sad	_____	_____

Directions Circle each word with a suffix, and write its base word on the line.

1. Our cat, Ricket, wrapped itself into a ball. _____

2. Ricket sat on the windowsill and napped. _____

3. Ricket will be resting until bedtime! _____

LESSON 33: Words that double the final consonant to add a suffix

Directions Form a new word by putting each base word and suffix together. Write the new word on the line.

Rule When a one-syllable short-vowel word ends in a single consonant, double the consonant before adding a suffix that begins with a vowel.

1. slim + er _____
2. flat + er _____
3. bold + est _____
4. run + ing _____
5. grin + ed _____
6. scrub + ed _____
7. drip + ing _____
8. plot + ed _____
9. swim + ing _____
10. hot + est _____

Directions Complete each sentence with one of the new words you formed above. Then circle the base word in the word you wrote.

1. Diane, an explorer, set out on her _____ adventure.

2. On the _____ day of the summer, she departed.

3. She had _____ her course on a map.

4. Diane would be _____ during parts of the journey.

5. She would move easily over the _____ terrain.

6. When she reached the river, she would do some _____.

7. The sun would quickly dry her _____ clothes.

8. Glad to be starting, Diane whistled happily and _____.

LESSON 33: Words that double the final consonant to add a suffix

Name _____

Rule When a word ends in silent **e**, drop the **e** before adding **y**. When a word ends in a single consonant preceded by a short vowel sound, double the consonant before adding **y**.

EXAMPLES

ic**e** + y = icy
fo**g** + y = foggy

Directions Form new words by adding the suffix **y** to each base word.

1. luck _____
2. crab _____
3. spice _____
4. edge _____
5. haste _____
6. chill _____

Rule The suffix **ly** can be added to many words to form a word that tells how.

EXAMPLE

soft + ly = softly

Directions Complete each sentence by adding **ly** to a word in the box. Write the new word on the line.

glad	loud	slow
quiet	serious	neat

1. Dana and Tad are _____ starting a baby-sitting business.

2. They take the job _____.

3. They _____ plan activities for the children.

4. When the baby naps, Tad asks the others not to play

_____.

5. Dana reminds the children to talk _____.

6. Before they go home, the children _____ put away their toys.

Rule When **ly** is added to a word ending in **le**, the **le** is dropped.

EXAMPLES

nimb**le** + ly = nimbly
feeb**le** + ly = feebly

Directions Read each clue. Find the word in the list that matches the clue. Then write the answer word in the crossword puzzle.

Across

1. a container for liquids
4. to make a high shrill sound by forcing breath through lips
5. having stones worn smooth and round
11. a flat figure with four sides and four right angles
13. the joint that connects the foot and the leg
14. doing something well

Down

1. a clasp on one end of a belt
2. to tread or step hard on
3. a stick of wax with a wick that gives light when burned
6. having bubbles
7. to scatter drops or bits
8. a mixture of red and blue
9. written carelessly
10. a large strong bird
12. a padded seat on a horse

whistle
bottle
trample
saddle
pebbly
rectangle
buckle
ankle
bubbly
sprinkle
purple
candle
scribbly
eagle
ably

LESSON 34: Words ending in LE; adding suffix -LY to words ending in LE

Name _____

Rule If a word ends in **y** preceded by a consonant, change the **y** to **i** and add **es**, **ed**, or **ly**. Do not change the **y** to **i** when adding the suffix **ing** or when adding **ly** to a one-syllable word that ends in **y** preceded by a consonant. If a word ends in **y** preceded by a vowel, just add the suffix.

EXAMPLES

cr**y** + es = cries
cr**y** + ing = crying
happ**y** + ly = happily
dr**y** + ly = dryly
enj**oy** + s = enjoys

Directions Form a new word by combining each base word and suffix. Write the new word on the line.

1. fly + es _____
2. employ + s _____
3. dirty + er _____
4. coy + ly _____
5. fly + ing _____
6. happy + ly _____

Directions Circle each word with a suffix and a base word that ends in **y**. Then write the base word on the line.

1. We were all studying together at the library. _____
2. Helen multiplied numbers on her calculator. _____
3. Tomás copied over his rough draft. _____
4. I shyly asked a librarian for help. _____
5. The librarian said he enjoyed helping me. _____

LESSON 35: Adding suffixes to words ending in Y

Directions Form a new word by putting each base word and suffix together. Write the new word on the line. Remember the rules for adding suffixes.

1. return + ing _____
2. hum + ing _____
3. relay + ed _____
4. quiet + est _____
5. haste + y _____
6. lease + ed _____
7. probable + ly _____
8. wet + est _____
9. bubble + ly _____

10. hot + er _____
11. plot + ed _____
12. clean + ed _____
13. fog + y _____
14. wave + ing _____
15. merry + ly _____
16. dry + es _____
17. saddle + ed _____
18. shy + ly _____

Directions Fill in the circle beside the word that completes each sentence.

1. We ___ up the horses for a ride in the desert.
   ○ saddleed   ○ saddled   ○ saddlied

2. The guide showed us how she ___ our trip on the map.
   ○ plotted   ○ plotied   ○ ploted

3. She said the desert is ___ during the day than at night.
   ○ hoter   ○ hotter   ○ hotier

4. We started ___ our hats as we set off on the trip.
   ○ waving   ○ waveing   ○ waveeing

5. Soon, we were ___ and singing songs.
   ○ huing   ○ huming   ○ humming

6. The guide told us we would ___ stop for lunch later.
   ○ probablely   ○ probably   ○ probabley

7. When we stopped, we drank some cold ___ water.
   ○ bubbly   ○ bubblely   ○ bubblly

8. After lunch, we ___ up the eating area.
   ○ cleanned   ○ cleaned   ○ cleanied

Name _____

Directions Circle the suffix in each word.

1. payment
2. needless
3. hopeful
4. fearless
5. goodness
6. statement
7. fairness
8. gladness
9. thankful
10. darkness
11. mindful
12. shipment
13. development
14. restful
15. greatness
16. government

Directions Form a new word by putting each base word and suffix together. Write the new word on the line. Then use the words you wrote to complete the sentence.

1. equip + ment _____
2. help + ful _____
3. peace + ful _____
4. spot + less _____
5. cold + ness _____
6. assign + ment _____
7. cheer + ful _____
8. hope + less _____
9. care + ful _____
10. kind + ness _____
11. bright + ness _____
12. enjoy + ment _____

13. The newly fallen snow was _____ and fluffy.

14. It was quiet and _____ in the country.

15. The _____ of the snow hurt my eyes.

16. The _____ of the air nipped my nose.

17. I had my ski _____ with me.

18. The ski instructor gave me some _____ tips.

Rule The suffixes **able**, **age**, and **ance** slightly change the meanings of words.

EXAMPLES
wash + able = wash**able** (can be washed)
marry + age = marri**age** (the result of marrying)
annoy + ance = annoy**ance** (the state of being annoyed)

Directions Form a new word by putting the base word and suffix together. Write the new word on the line. Remember the rules for adding suffixes.

1. pass + age _____
2. beat + able _____
3. enjoy + able _____
4. avail + able _____
5. disturb + ance _____
6. remit + ance _____
7. bag + age _____
8. short + age _____

Directions Complete each sentence by adding **able**, **age**, or **ance** to a base word in the box.

| post | value | insure | assist | break | accept | pack | reason |

1. We carried the _____ to the Post Office.

2. The clerk asked if we needed _____.

3. We wanted to know if the box was _____ for mailing.

4. We asked how much _____ was needed to mail the box.

5. "Are the contents _____?" asked the clerk.

6. "You might want to buy _____ for the contents."

7. "You can buy it for a _____ cost."

LESSON 36: Suffixes -ABLE, -AGE, -ANCE

Name _____

Rule The suffixes **en**, **ity**, **ive**, and **some** change the way a base word is used.

EXAMPLES
gold + en = gold**en** (to make or become like gold)
humid + ity = humid**ity** (the quality of being humid)
act + ive = act**ive** (full of action)
lone + some = lone**some** (having a lonely feeling)

Directions Form a new word by putting the base word and suffix together.

1. detect + ive _____
2. whole + some _____
3. sad + en _____
4. disrupt + ive _____
5. tire + some _____
6. sharp + en _____
7. national + ity _____
8. universe + ity _____

Directions Read each sentence and find the picture that goes with it. Write the number of the sentence on the line under the picture. Then circle each word that contains **ity**, **en**, **ive**, or **some**.

1. The massive hot air balloon was awesome.

2. The broken lamp suggested the possibility of foul play.

3. The speaker was impressive and not tiresome.

4. The quarrelsome cat jumped on the wooden box.

5. The creative artist painted an impressive golden sun.

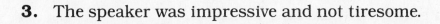

_____   _____   _____   _____

Rule Often the suffixes **ion**, **tion**, and **sion** are added to base words. These suffixes mean the act, condition, or result of something.

EXAMPLES

correct + **ion** = correction
invade + **sion** = invasion
create + **tion** = creation

Directions Read the words in the box. Underline each word in which you see **tion**. Circle each word in which you see **sion**. Then complete the sentences using the words in the box.

education	direction	discussion	division
protection	collision	operation	pollution
election	television	subtraction	donation

1. The students at Oak Park School receive a fine _____.

2. First graders learn to solve simple _____ problems.

3. Fourth graders learn that following a _____ is important.

4. Sixth graders will have a _____ about the government.

5. They will see a film about the _____ of a president.

6. The film will be on _____.

7. In science, fifth graders read about _____.

8. Some students are doing reports on the _____ of animals.

LESSON 37: Suffixes -ION, -TION, -SION

Name ______________________________

Rule The suffix **ward** means in the direction of or toward.

EXAMPLES

back + ward = back**ward** (toward the back)
home + ward = home**ward** (in the directon of home)

Directions Read the sentence in each box. Draw a picture to show what the sentence means. Then circle the words in each sentence that have the suffix **ward**.

1. Kurt looked upward and saw a colorful balloon drifting toward him.

2. Mother stopped the car from rolling backward down the hill.

3. The hikers carefully climbed downward from the top of the mountain.

4. The band marched forward, toward the center of the town.

Directions You will often read words that have more than one suffix. Each word in the list below has two suffixes. In each word, underline the first suffix and circle the second suffix.

1. carefully
2. sharpened
3. seemingly
4. surprisingly
5. alarmingly
6. frightening
7. cheerfulness
8. heartened
9. saddened
10. handsomely
11. actively
12. flattened

Directions Circle each word with more than one suffix. Then write the base word on the line.

1. Our trip to the museum went surprisingly quickly. _____

2. We appreciated the thoughtfulness of our guide. _____

3. The guide told us to study the exhibits carefully. _____

4. The dinosaur exhibit was attractively displayed. _____

5. Some of the skeletons were alarmingly huge. _____

6. A live mammoth would have been frightening. _____

7. The guide involved us actively in discussions. _____

8. We were saddened when it was time to leave. _____

LESSON 38: Words with more than one suffix

Name _____

Italy	sadly	stillness	shivered	tiresome
deepen	age	needless	spotless	management
edit	icy	nineteen	seventeen	middle
roses	oboe	sun	lilacs	arm
dryly	probably	darkness	grazing	wobbly

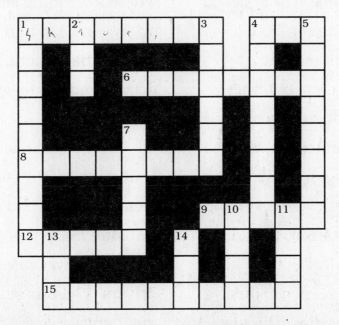

Across
1. shook with cold
4. shines and gives warmth
6. causing boredom
8. comes after eighteen
9. sweet-smelling flowers
12. unhappily
15. people who run a business

Down
1. quietness
2. slippery
3. make deeper
4. perfectly clean
5. not necessary
7. country in Europe
10. musical instrument
11. prepare for publication
13. a limb of your body
14. how long you've lived

Directions Read the story. Draw a heavy line on the map that will show the order in which Skip and Carol passed the places mentioned in the story. Then, circle all the words in the story that have suffixes.

Sightseeing

Skip Hark has an older sister named Carol. With some of her inheritance, Carol purchased a beautiful sports car. When Carol invited Skip to take a ride he gladly offered his acceptance. They backed out of the driveway and moved speedily along the pavement.

At the railroad crossing, they waited for a locomotive to pass by. Then Carol drove on toward the gas station. There they purchased some car repair equipment.

From the gas station, they drove past the monument where the war battle had once taken place. Just past the monument, Carol luckily steered clear of a reckless driver. Next they went by the university buildings. On the steps of the police station a detective was arresting someone. They passed a church where a wedding ceremony was going on. When Skip and Carol reached the river embankment, it began to drizzle and get foggy. So they headed homeward.

On the way back, they saw some confusion by the roadside. The reckless driver had been in a collision. Skip was proud of his sister. She was one of the ablest of drivers. The excursion had been most enjoyable.

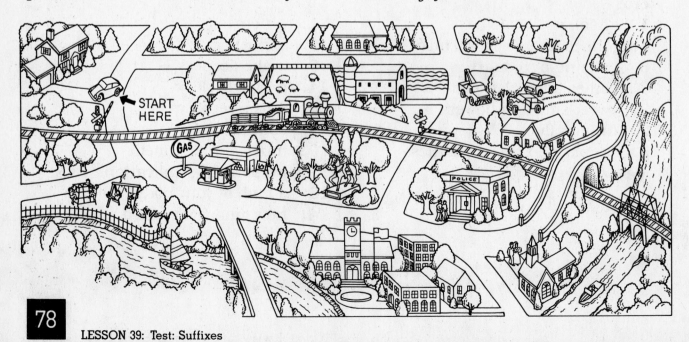

Name _____

Rule A suffix is a syllable in itself if it contains a vowel sound.

	Vowels Seen	Vowel Sounds	Syllables		Vowels Seen	Vowel Sounds	Syllables
heavily	___	___	___	curly	___	___	___
carrier	___	___	___	happiness	___	___	___
cheer	___	___	___	sleepier	___	___	___
fanciest	___	___	___	cloudy	___	___	___
pities	___	___	___	handsome	___	___	___
available	___	___	___	paying	___	___	___
storage	___	___	___	nationality	___	___	___
carrying	___	___	___	equipment	___	___	___
employment	___	___	___	insurance	___	___	___
disruptive	___	___	___	fog	___	___	___
dust	___	___	___	destroying	___	___	___
readiness	___	___	___	collision	___	___	___
sharpen	___	___	___	rectangle	___	___	___
humidity	___	___	___	longingly	___	___	___
northward	___	___	___	defensive	___	___	___
buckle	___	___	___	lucky	___	___	___
hedge	___	___	___	laughter	___	___	___
rehearse	___	___	___	spaghetti	___	___	___
shoulder	___	___	___	sailor	___	___	___
mosquito	___	___	___	conscious	___	___	___

Directions Study the rules. Then divide the words into syllables, using hyphens.

Rule 1 A one-syllable word is never divided.

EXAMPLES
boat   good   knelt   smell

Rule 2 Divide a compound word between the words that make up the compound word.

EXAMPLES
pan-cake   sun-set
air-plane   base-ball

Rule 3 When a word has a suffix, divide the word between the base word and the suffix.

EXAMPLES
melt-ed   soft-ness
sew-ing   home-less

Rule 4 When a word ends in **le** preceded by a consonant, divide the word before that consonant. When a word ends in **ckle**, divide between the **k** and the **le**.

EXAMPLES
tur-tle   ca-ble   this-tle
pick-le   tack-le   speck-le

1. thumbtack _____
2. purple _____
3. handle _____
4. earthquake _____
5. deepen _____
6. curly _____
7. pickle _____
8. skyward _____
9. useful _____
10. apple _____
11. mumble _____
12. helpless _____
13. steering _____
14. payment _____
15. headache _____
16. tickle _____
17. sickness _____
18. peaches _____
19. handsome _____
20. safest _____
21. postage _____
22. shipwreck _____
23. knuckle _____
24. thistle _____
25. blacksmith _____
26. angle _____

LESSON 40: Syllables in compound words, suffixed words, words ending in LE

Name _____

Directions Use the words in the box to find the name for each picture. Write each name on the line under its picture.

Rule If a syllable has two vowels, the first vowel usually stands for a long sound and the second is silent.

toad	train	hay	beads	creature	nails
crow	daisy	queen	sheep	toes	cheese

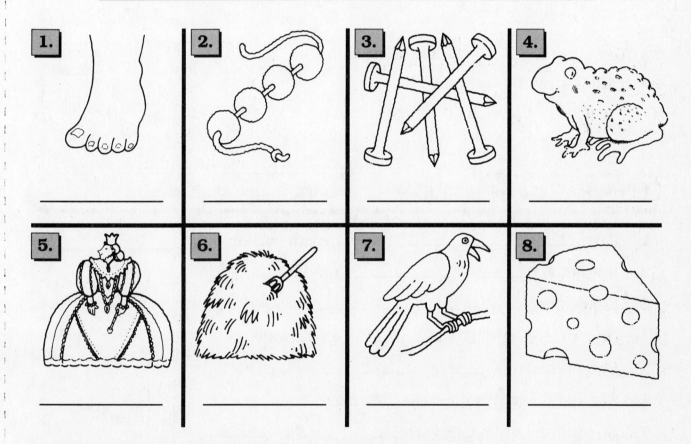

1. _____

2. _____

3. _____

4. _____

5. _____

6. _____

7. _____

8. _____

Directions Complete each sentence with a word from the box at the top of the page.

1. Our class rode a _____ to visit a farm.

2. At the farm we saw cows and _____.

3. We saw the farmer put up a strange _____ in the field.

4. The creature was a scarecrow with a _____ in its hat.

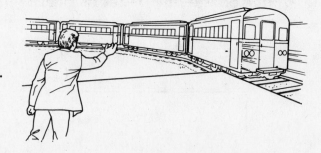

1. Jay wanted to go straight home.
2. He had to wait in line to get a ticket.
3. Jay failed to get on the train.

1. A gray donkey strayed into the daylight.
2. It went straight to the hay.
3. The donkey brayed as it raided the hay.

Directions Complete each sentence with a word from the box.

1. Fay _____ that her room was dreary.
2. It was too _____ and dark.
3. Fay decided to _____ her room.
4. She wanted light _____ walls.
5. She needed one _____ of paint.
6. She did one wall a different _____.
7. She wanted wallpaper with _____.
8. Fay painted her room on a _____ day.
9. She didn't _____ long to finish.
10. She fixed it up without _____.
11. She hung two pictures on _____.
12. She hung yellow curtains on her

_____ window.

bay
daisies
complained
rainy
plain
paint
pail
gray
wait
delay
way
nails

82

LESSON 41: Regular double vowels AI, AY

Name ____________________

Directions Circle the regular double vowels in each word that stand for a /ē/ sound. Then write each word in the correct column.

sneeze	meek	leisure	heed
keen	reach	seizure	neat
ceiling	peach	seize	reason

see	**leaf**	**Neil**
________	________	________
________	________	________
________	________	________
________	________	________

Directions Circle the word that correctly completes each sentence and write it on the line.

1. Peaches are ____________ this time of year. beaded / reach / cheap

2. Unripened peaches are ____________ and hard. mean / green / keen

3. People sometimes ____________ off the fuzzy skin. flee / lee / peel

4. Eat a juicy peach slowly and at your ____________. leisure / seizure / ceiling

tried	dried	ties	pried	pliers
fried	pies	supplies	cried	untied

1. People _____ out with joy when the circus arrived.

2. Everyone _____ to push forward to see the animals.

3. The owner told workers to unload the _____.

4. Meanwhile, the cook _____ chicken for dinner.

5. The baker made _____ for dessert.

6. After dinner, everyone washed and _____ the dishes.

7. Then three clowns wearing big, striped _____ put on a show.

8. One clown _____ a rope from a big box.

9. The other clown used _____ to pull out the nails.

10. Another clown popped out when the lid was _____ off.

LESSON 42: Regular double vowel IE

Name _____

Rule The double vowels **oa, oe, ow** usually have the /ō/ sound.

EXAMPLES

r**oa**d   t**oe**   bl**ow**

Directions Say each word in the box. Circle the regular double vowels that stand for the /ō/ sound. Then write each word in the correct column.

hoe	snow	float	pillow	toe
bowl	poach	foe	boast	doe
row	throat	soap	woe	bow

coat   **Joe**   **crow**

_____   _____   _____

_____   _____   _____

_____   _____   _____

_____   _____   _____

_____   _____   _____

Directions Match each definition with a word from the box at the top of the page.

1. used when you swallow   _____

2. something soft for your head   _____

3. a garden tool   _____

4. hair ribbon   _____

5. one way to cook eggs   _____

6. sadness   _____

7. one way to move a boat   _____

8. what you eat cereal from   _____

9. something to wash with   _____

85

LESSON 43: Regular double vowels OA, OE, OW

tomorrow	pleased	speak	seeds
main	due	row	straight
goat	peek	hoe	boast
continue	narrow	receive	need

1. A gardener will _____ to the class about planting.

2. We will _____ planting flowers today.

3. Then _____ we will plant vegetables.

4. A report about gardening will be _____ next week.

5. You will need to buy _____.

6. Use a _____ to dig up the dirt.

7. Complete one _____ before starting another.

8. Make sure the rows are _____, not too wide.

9. The rows should also be _____, not crooked.

10. The _____ thing to remember is to water the seeds.

11. Seeds will grow if they _____ water and get sun.

12. Soon, little plants will _____ out of the soil.

13. You will be able to _____ about your garden.

14. Do not let a _____ get into the garden.

15. You will not be _____ if that happens.

16. You _____ a fence to keep animals out.

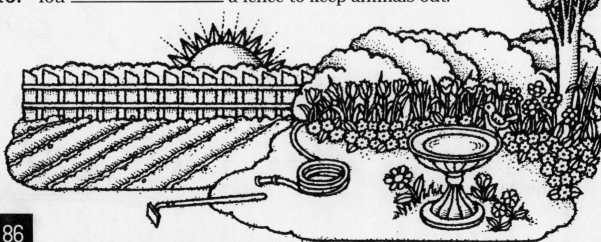

LESSON 43: Review: Regular double vowels

Name _____

Rule The vowel digraph **ea** can stand for the /e/ sound.

EXAMPLES

st**ea**dy   l**ea**ther   sw**ea**t

Directions Say the name of each picture. Circle the picture if you hear the /e/ sound in its name.

Directions Complete each sentence with a word from the box at the right.

1. The _____ was windy and cool.

2. Beth got _____ to go outside.

3. She wanted to remain _____.

4. She put a hat on her _____.

5. She took out her _____ gloves.

6. She wore her favorite _____.

7. Beth needed _____ to mend the sweater.

8. She used the needle with a _____ hand.

sweater

weather

thread

steady

ready

healthy

head

leather

Rule The vowel digraphs **ei** and **ey** can stand for the /ā/ sound.

EXAMPLES

w**ei**gh   fr**ei**ght   ob**ey**   sur**vey**

Directions Underline the vowel digraph that stands for the long a sound in each word in the box. Then write each word in the correct column.

eight	obey	sleigh	hey
neighbor	veil	prey	survey

reins

_____
_____
_____

they

_____
_____
_____

Directions Read the sentences and questions below. Answer each question with a response from the box.

watching and observing   rules

transmitted or sent out

1. The **reign** of King Henry lasted for many years. If a king **reigns,** what does he do?

_____

2. King Henry had royal guards keep his advisors under **surveillance.** What would the royal guards be doing to keep the advisors under **surveillance?**

_____

3. The royal guards **conveyed** the king's wishes and orders to the people. What does **conveyed** mean?

_____

88

LESSON 44: Vowel digraphs EI, EY

Name _____

EXAMPLES

gr**ie**f   p**ie**ce   sh**ie**ld

Directions Read each pair of sentences. Then underline each word in which **ie** stands for the /ē/ sound. Circle the number of the sentence that describes the picture.

1. Everyone was frightened for a brief moment.
2. It was a relief to know that the snake had been seized.

1. The cashier gave a piercing shriek as the thief escaped.
2. The thief was caught by the chief of police.

1. A diesel engine is used in many machines.
2. It helps a locomotive achieve unbelievable speeds.

Directions Circle the word that correctly completes each sentence, and write it on the line.

1. "I _____ we are in for a storm," said Elsie.

achieve
relieve
believe

2. "The weather report was _____ and to the point."

chief
brief
thief

3. "There will be _____ winds and hail."

pieces
shrieks
fierce

Directions Read each definition. Write the word from the box that matches the definition. Put a check (✓) beside the answer if the letters **ie** stand for the long /ē/ sound.

chief	field	mantelpiece	relieved	fielder	piece
shriek	priest	die	belief	fried	brief

1. a place where corn and wheat grow   _____

2. another word for *faith*   _____

3. a portion of something can also be called this _____

4. a loud, shrill sound   _____

5. eggs can be cooked this way   _____

6. the way you feel when news is good   _____

7. head person in the fire department   _____

8. what flowers do without water   _____

9. person whose work is in a church   _____

10. shelf on a fireplace   _____

11. a word that describes something short   _____

12. person on a baseball team   _____

LESSON 45: Vowel digraph IE

Name _____

Directions Say the name of each picture. Circle the picture if you hear the same vowel sound you hear in *too* and *moon*.

Rule One sound the vowel digraph **oo** can stand for is the vowel sound you hear in *too* and *moon*.

1.

2.

3.

4.

5.

6.

7.

8.

9.

10.

11.

12.

Directions Complete each sentence with a word from the box.

1. The rocket launch is set for _____ today.

2. We will watch it in our _____ .

3. A _____ rocket will help launch the spaceship.

4. The spaceship is going to the _____ .

5. It will make one _____ before landing.

6. It will send back pictures as _____ .

proof

loop

noon

classroom

booster

moon

Directions Read the word in each box. Then draw a picture that shows what the word means.

1.

book

2.

football

3.

foot

4.

hood

5.

woods

6.

hook

Directions Complete each sentence with a word from the box.

notebook	looked	barefoot	shook
crook	cook	hook	stood

1. The detective hung her coat on the _____ by the door.

2. She sat down to check the notes in her _____.

3. She _____ her head in anger.

4. The _____ she was after had escaped.

5. The detective _____ up and walked to the window.

6. She _____ down at the dark empty street.

LESSON 46: Vowel digraph OO

Name _____

Directions Read the words in the box. Then write each word in the correct column.

Rule The vowel digraph **oo** can stand for the vowel sound you hear in *too* or the vowel sound you hear in *look*.

bloom	cook	wood	cool	shook
troop	soot	roost	stood	spoon

too   **look**

_____   _____
_____   _____
_____   _____
_____   _____
_____   _____

Directions Read each sentence. Circle each word in which **oo** stands for the vowel sound you hear in *too*. Underline each word in which **oo** stands for the sound you hear in *look*.

1. The little crook was looking for food.

2. It scooted into the yard and shook the cans.

3. The campers in the wooden cabin were spooked.

4. They stood quietly in the small room.

5. The cook grabbed a broom.

6. It was a cool night with a full moon.

7. The campers looked out into the moonlit night.

8. They felt like fools when their crook was a raccoon.

93

LESSON 47: Vowel digraph OO

A Walk in the Woods

Leslie and Carrie Underwood put on their boots and took a moonlight walk after the heavy rainfall. The blooming flowers in the yard drooped from the rain. The kids set out down the footpath and into the woods. Along the path, the moonlight shined on mushrooms and toadstools. A raccoon snooped around the dogwood trees. Leslie and Carrie crossed a brook and passed the house of a woodcutter. They came out of the woods on the other side of a grove of cottonwood trees.

Soon the kids came to the smooth sandy shore of a lagoon. Many little creatures lived there in nooks and holes. Nearby they took a look at an insect emerging from its cocoon. A coot or a loon, they were not sure which, swooped down on the deck of a sloop anchored in the lagoon.

It began to grow cool, so Leslie and Carrie trooped back home. Suddenly Carrie let out a whoop. Something wet and furry had scooted past her. They guessed it was a woodchuck who had been looking for food.

1. What word tells you it was nighttime? _____

2. What snooped around the dogwoods? _____

3. What body of water did the girls come upon? _____

4. What kind of boat was anchored there? _____

5. Name two birds you read about. _____

94

LESSON 47: Vowel digraph OO

Name _____

Directions Circle the name of each picture.

Rule The vowel digraphs **aw** and **au** stand for the same sound. They stand for the vowel sound you hear in *draw* and *August*.

1.

autumn
laundry
naughty

2.
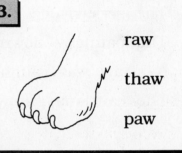
draw
dawn
thaw

3.
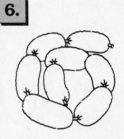
raw
thaw
paw

4.
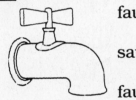
fault
saucer
faucet

5.
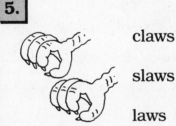
claws
slaws
laws

6.
sausages
saucer
applause

Directions Complete each sentence with a word from the box.

autumn	hawk	awkward	claws
caught	paused	author	hauled

1. It was _____, and the leaves had changed colors.

2. The large bird _____ and waited for the right moment.

3. Then the _____ swooped down and seized its prey.

4. It had _____ its dinner.

5. The hawk is not _____, but very graceful in flight.

6. Its _____ are sharp and powerful.

7. The hawk _____ the food back to its nest.

LESSON 48: Vowel digraphs AU, AW

Directions Read each sentence and find the picture that goes with it at the bottom of the page. Write the number of the sentence on the line under the picture. Then circle the words that contain **au** and **aw**.

1. A jaunty dinosaur draws a picture.

2. The saucy leprechaun does a somersault.

3. The haunted house looks gaudy.

4. A haughty fawn is sprawled on the ice.

5. The scrawny cat slept in a drawer.

6. The paunchy clown sat on the lawn and bawled.

7. A straw was caught in the faucet.

8. The cautious puppy gnawed a bone.

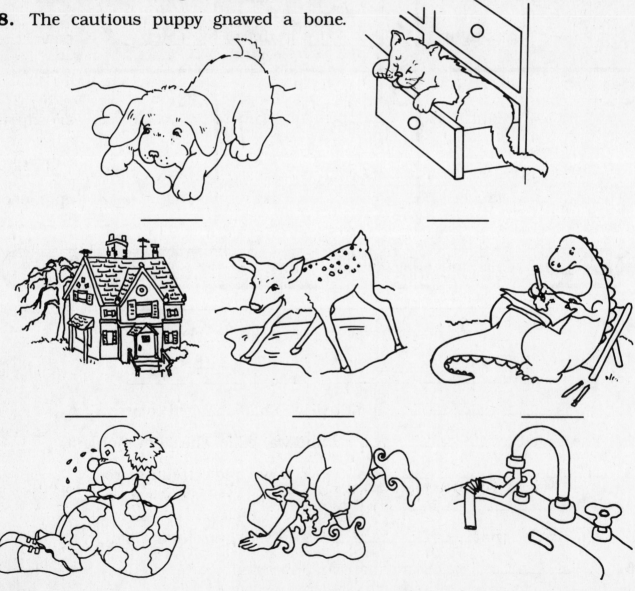

LESSON 48: Vowel digraphs AU, AW

Directions Play Tick-Tack-Toe. In each game, find the three pictures in a straight or diagonal line whose names have the same vowel sound. Draw a straight line through these pictures.

LESSON 49: Vowel digraphs

1. Kay ___ when she saw the snow.   shrieked   shawl
                                                 O   O

2. The mountain ___ looked like cotton.   pieces   peaks
                                                 O   O

3. The ___ looked like white blankets.   faults   fields
                                                 O   O

4. Kay put her hood over her ___.   head   heed
                                                 O   O

5. She was going for a ___ ride.   sleigh   slaw
                                                 O   O

6. The sleigh was pulled by a ___ horse.   gray   green
                                                 O   O

7. Kay ___ onto the front seat.   creaked   crawled
                                                 O   O

8. The driver tugged on the ___.   chiefs   reins
                                                 O   O

9. The horse ___ and galloped away.   obeyed   believed
                                                 O   O

10. The space ___ was set.   leash   launch
                                                 O   O

11. It would take place at ___.   dawn   draw
                                                 O   O

12. There were ___ scientists in the rocket. eat   eight
                                                 O   O

13. They were headed for the ___.   meat   moon
                                                 O   O

14. There was a ___ moment of quiet.   breeze   brief
                                                 O   O

15. The rocket ___ sounded like thunder.   boot   boom
                                                 O   O

16. The blastoff was ___ and on time.   gaudy   good
                                                 O   O

17. The crew was ___ and happy.   relieved gloomy
                                                 O   O

LESSON 48: Test: Vowel digraphs

Name _____

Directions Under each picture write the word from the list that goes with it.

Definition A **diphthong** is made up of two vowels sounded so both vowels blend together as one sound. The diphthongs **oi** and **oy** stand for the same sound. They stand for the vowel sound you hear in *coin* and *boy*.

boil	noise	coins	royalty
soil	boy	cowboy	

1.

_____

2.

_____

3.

_____

4.

_____

5.

_____

6.

_____

7.

_____

Directions For each word, write the letter of the definition in the second column on the line beside the word.

1. loyal _____   A. slightly damp

2. embroider _____   B. light, bluish green color

3. voyage _____   C. make a design on cloth with needle and thread

4. moist _____   D. faithful

5. broil _____   E. a long trip to a place far away

6. poison _____   F. something that can cause death

7. annoy _____   G. bother or pester

8. turquoise _____   H. a way to cook something

The Busy Day

It had rained during the night, but Floyd wasn't disappointed. Instead, he was joyful! Now the soil would be moist for weeding and digging. Floyd jumped out of bed and put on his corduroy pants and turquoise sweatshirt. He rushed downstairs to join his noisy brothers and sisters for breakfast. He boiled an egg and broiled some bacon. With a pocketful of coins, he set off for the garden supply store.

When Floyd returned, he toiled all day with his poinsettias. Rejoicing at their size, he tied the plants to pointed sticks that he stuck into the soil. He did this by coiling string around the plant stems. He made sure the ground was moist. Floyd enjoyed this kind of work. Later he picked some fresh corn which his mom would brush with cooking oil and bake in foil.

"This fresh corn is a good vegetable choice for dinner," Floyd's mom said in a pleasant voice. "With everything else I've planned, we'll have a royal meal."

1. Floyd felt good because of the rain. Which word tells you he felt good? _____

2. What color was Floyd's sweatshirt? _____

3. What plants did Floyd like to grow? _____

4. In what did Mom bake the corn? _____

Name _____

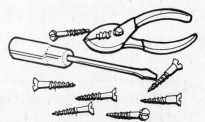

1. The crew threw down their coats.
2. Their new screws and tools were on the ground.

1. The new team drew cheers.
2. Newton's nephew threw a pass.

1. The new rocket flew off into space.
2. The crowd knew the crew would be in the news.

Directions Complete each sentence with a word from the box.

slew	knew	shrewd	blew
threw	jewel	drew	stew

1. The _____ knight crept up on the dragon.
2. The knight _____ his sword.
3. The dragon _____ sparks of fire.
4. The knight _____ the dragon was not friendly.
5. The knight _____ the sword on the ground and ran.

1. loyal
2. Joyce
3. jewel
4. noisy
5. annoy
6. chew
7. spoiled
8. soil
9. nephew
10. poison
11. employ
12. threw
13. destroy
14. coin
15. stew
16. point
17. oil
18. royal
19. dew
20. moist
21. newspaper
22. screws
23. avoid
24. flew

Directions Read each sentence. Think about the way the first two words are related. Then choose one of the words from above to complete the analogy.

1. **Hammer** is to **nails** as **screwdriver** is to _____.

2. **Vegetables** are to **salad** as **meat** is to _____.

3. **Desert** is to **dry** as **swamp** is to _____.

4. **Niece** is to **girl** as _____ is to **boy.**

5. **Dollar** is to **bill** as **quarter** is to _____.

6. **Milk** is to **sip** as **apple** is to _____.

7. **Dismiss** is to **fire** as **hire** is to _____.

8. **Radio** is to **listen** as _____ is to **read.**

9. **Hay** is to **horse** as _____ is to **machine.**

10. **Fresh** is to **food** as _____ is to **garbage.**

11. **Whisper** is to **quiet** as **shout** is to _____.

12. **Run** is to **ran** as **throw** is to _____.

13. **Build** is to **create** as **demolish** is to _____.

14. **Tip** is to **brush** as _____ is to **pencil.**

15. **See** is to **saw** as **fly** is to _____.

16. **Ice** is to **frost** as **water** is to _____.

17. **Grass** is to **lawn** as **dirt** is to _____.

Name _____

Directions Circle the name of each picture.

1.

claw   clown

2.

bless   blouse

3. 1000

thousand   thaw

4.

shower   shout

5.

floors   flowers

6.

cloud   clods

Directions Read the sentences and questions below. Answer each question with a response from the box.

a boat used to haul cargo	drenched
disorderly and rough	looked angry

1. The crew on the boat was **rowdy** and had to be quieted down. What does **rowdy** mean?

_____

2. The crew was on a **scow** that was hauling garbage down the river. What is a **scow?**

_____

3. The crew was **doused** when a sudden storm blew up. What does **doused** mean?

_____

4. The captain **scowled** at the behavior of the crew. What did the captain do if he **scowled?**

_____

Directions Complete each sentence with a word from the box.

1. There wasn't a _____ in the sky.

2. We were going to climb the _____.

3. Grandpa said he would _____ for a campsite.

4. We were _____ to bring only a few things.

5. We would sleep on the _____.

6. That night we heard a _____ sound.

7. We all thought that it was a _____ bear.

8. The next morning we went _____ the mountain.

down
howling
cloud
brown
mountain
scout
allowed
ground

---

1. The _____ was celebrating.

2. There was a _____ gathering.

3. People surrounded the _____ in the park.

4. They were _____ and noisy.

5. The town _____ was dedicating the fountain.

6. The mayor _____ to five.

7. The crowd _____ and clapped.

8. The people were _____ of their town.

fountain
proud
council
town
counted
shouted
crowd
rowdy

LESSON 52: Diphthongs OU, OW

Name _____

Directions Read each sentence. Circle each word in which **ow** stands for the vowel sound you hear in *cow*. Underline each word in which **ow** stands for the vowel sound you hear in *snow*. Then write each **ow** word in the correct column.

Rule The diphthong **ow** stands for the vowel sound you hear in *cow*. The letters **ow** can also stand for the vowel sound you hear in *snow*.

1. Do you know that tomorrow is the party?
2. No one will be allowed in without a costume.
3. I will be a clown wearing a big bow.
4. Ted is going to show up as a flower in a bowl.
5. Kim is going to be a brown owl.
6. She will borrow a pillow to stuff in her costume.
7. Dad said we should be mellow, not rowdy.
8. Anyhow, the band will drown out our noise.

ow as in cow   **ow as in snow**

_____   _____
_____   _____
_____   _____
_____   _____
_____   _____
_____   _____

LESSON 53: Diphthong OW

Directions Read the sentence in each box and then draw a picture to show what the sentence means. Circle the words with diphthongs in each sentence.

1. The frowning clown was employed to make the crowd of thousands howl with joy.

2. The shrewd cowboy pounced on the steer while avoiding the points of his long horns.

3. The noisy nephew was annoying his aunt when he pointed and shouted at the flower show.

4. The powerful royal family threw coins from a tower into a fountain.

LESSON 53: Diphthongs OI, OY, EW, OU, OW

Name _____

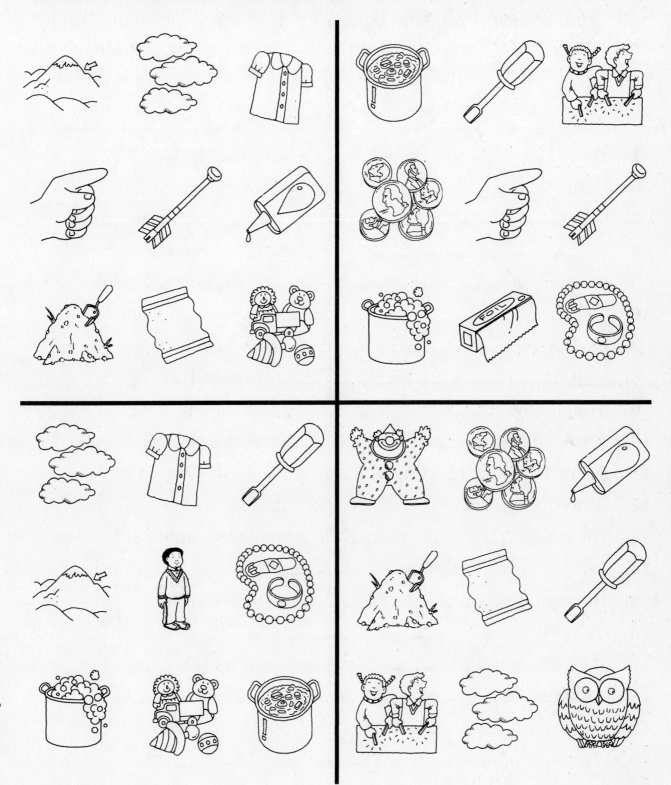

pounce	borrow	down	out
growled	disappointed	joy	know
show	followed	sound	knew
howled	threw	boy	toy
avoid	enjoyed	loud	join

1. The _____ couldn't wait to open the big box.

2. He didn't _____ what could be in it.

3. "What kind of _____ is so big?" he wondered.

4. He _____ the paper and ribbons aside.

5. He whooped for _____ when he saw the toy.

6. He _____ right away it was the robot he wanted.

7. He lifted it _____ of the box.

8. He put it _____ and turned it on.

9. It made a very _____ noise.

10. The boy's dog _____ at the robot.

11. He tried to _____ on it.

12. He was frightened by its _____.

13. The robot _____ the dog all around the house.

14. The dog tried but couldn't _____ the robot.

15. The boy _____ with laughter.

16. He was not _____ at all.

17. The boy _____ his new robot.

18. "I will _____ my toy to all my friends," said the boy.

19. "They can _____ me and play with it."

20. "They'll probably want to _____ it."

Name _____

EXAMPLES

br**ea**d   **oi**ntment

Directions Say each word. Write the double vowel on the first line. Then write the number of syllables you hear on the second line.

	Double Vowel	Number of Syllables			Double Vowel	Number of Syllables
1. instead	____	____	19. loyal	____	____
2. noisy	____	____	20. double	____	____
3. repeat	____	____	21. moisten	____	____
4. thought	____	____	22. appear	____	____
5. haunted	____	____	23. breakfast	____	____
6. wealthy	____	____	24. piece	____	____
7. spoonful	____	____	25. ounce	____	____
8. receive	____	____	26. because	____	____
9. jewelry	____	____	27. straight	____	____
10. awkward	____	____	28. pillow	____	____
11. lied	____	____	29. soup	____	____
12. chief	____	____	30. eighty	____	____
13. moonlight	____	____	31. touch	____	____
14. house	____	____	32. soul	____	____
15. avenue	____	____	33. laundry	____	____
16. withdraw	____	____	34. annoy	____	____
17. flow	____	____	35. true	____	____
18. dainty	____	____	36. blooming	____	____

LESSON 55: Syllables in words containing double vowels

Rule When double vowels stand for one vowel sound, do not divide the word between the two vowels.

EXAMPLES

por-tr**ai**t	s**ei**ze
fl**ow**-er	r**ea**-son

Rule When two vowels are sounded separately, divide the word between the two vowels.

EXAMPLES

ra-d**i**-**o**	d**i**-**e**t
cr**u**-**e**l	i-d**e**-**a**

Directions Underline the double vowels in the words. If the double vowels stand for one sound, write **1** on the line. If the double vowels are sounded separately, write **2** on the line. Then divide the words into syllables using hyphens.

	Double Vowel Sounds	Syllables		Double Vowel Sounds	Syllables
dialect	___	_____	poison	___	_____
couch	___	_____	diagnose	___	_____
create	___	_____	dinosaur	___	_____
quiet	___	_____	area	___	_____
tower	___	_____	saucer	___	_____
thousand	___	_____	diary	___	_____
ideas	___	_____	casual	___	_____
screw	___	_____	season	___	_____
loudest	___	_____	raccoons	___	_____
defiant	___	_____	riot	___	_____
royalty	___	_____	survey	___	_____
realize	___	_____	situate	___	_____
shriek	___	_____	pheasant	___	_____
headline	___	_____	cereal	___	_____
diesel	___	_____	really	___	_____

LESSON 55: Syllables in words with two vowels

Name _____

Directions Write the plural form of each word.

Rule When a word is in its plural form, it means more than one. If a word ends in **ss, z, x, sh,** or **ch,** the suffix **es** is usually added to make the word plural.

1. tax _____
2. buzz _____
3. branch _____
4. waltz _____
5. glass _____
6. fox _____

7. guess _____
8. patch _____

Directions Underline one word in each sentence that has the suffix **es**. Write its base word on the line.

1. The forecaster takes off her glasses. _____
2. The mountain passes are closed due to snow. _____
3. There are patches of ice on every road. _____
4. Ten more inches of snow fell last night. _____
5. The snow covers the bushes and trees. _____
6. The forecaster has two wishes. _____
7. You have two guesses what she wants. _____
8. She wants bright sunshine and warm sandy beaches. _____

111

LESSON 56: Plural form for words ending in SS, Z, X, SH, CH

Rule If a word ends in **y** preceded by a consonant, change the **y** to **i** and add **es** to form the plural. If **y** is preceded by a vowel, just add **s**.

EXAMPLES

activity = activit**ies**
chimney = chimney**s**

Directions Write the plural form of each word.

1. fly _____
3. tray _____
5. hobby _____
7. melody _____

2. mystery _____
4. beauty _____
6. medley _____
8. injury _____

Directions Complete each sentence with the plural form of the word at the right.

1. It is fun to explore the _____ near your home.   (library)

2. Which _____ do you enjoy reading?   (story)

3. I enjoy reading _____.   (mystery)

4. I also like books about _____.   (spy)

5. Some children like books about _____.   (cowboy)

6. Some like to read about sports _____.   (victory)

7. My sister likes to read about lawyers and _____.   (jury)

8. Do you enjoy books about other _____?   (country)

LESSON 56: Plural form for words ending in Y

Name _____

Rule If a word ends in **f** or **fe**, usually change the **f** or **fe** to **v** and add **es** to form the plural.

EXAMPLES

wolf = wol**ves**
wife = wi**ves**

Directions Write the plural form of each word.

1. half _____   2. thief _____

3. life _____   4. shelf _____

5. knife _____   6. calf _____

7. loaf _____   8. elf _____

Directions Write a word from the box below to complete each sentence. Then write its base word on the line.

shelves	hooves	wolves	thieves
lives	loaves	calves	wives

1. Farmers of long ago led very busy _____.   _____

2. They rose early to tend to their cows and

   _____.   _____

3. They made horseshoes for their horses'

   _____.   _____

4. They put up fences to keep out the packs of

   _____.   _____

5. These animals were _____ that   _____
   stole the farmers' chickens.

6. The farmers' _____ worked very hard, too.   _____

7. They cooked the meals and baked _____   _____
   of bread.

8. They filled the _____ with jars of   _____
   vegetables and homemade jam.

113

Rule If a word ends in **o**, add **s** to form the plural. Some words, such as potato, tomato, hero, and buffalo, are made plural by adding **es**.

EXAMPLES

kimono = kimono**s**
tornado = tornado**es**

Directions Write the plural of each word in the list below. Then choose either the singular or plural form of a word to complete the sentences below.

1. kangaroo _____
2. rodeo _____
3. piano _____
4. lasso _____
5. solo _____
6. sombrero _____
7. soprano _____
8. bronco _____
9. hero _____
10. buffalo _____

1. The _____ came to town.

2. A singer sang a _____ to open the show.

3. Cowhands were going to ride bucking _____.

4. They waved their _____ in the air.

5. Then one stood on two huge _____.

6. One buffalo jumped as high as a _____.

7. Some riders wore _____ on their heads.

8. Rodeo stars can be real _____ to children.

LESSON 57: Plural form for words ending in O

Name _____

Rule Some words form their plurals in an unusual way.

EXAMPLES
goose—geese   mouse—mice

Directions Write each plural form beside the correct singular form.

oxen	mice	women	men
feet	children	teeth	geese

1. man _____

2. foot _____

3. ox _____

4. woman _____

5. mouse _____

6. child _____

7. goose _____

8. tooth _____

Rule For some words, the singular and plural forms are the same.

EXAMPLES
sheep   deer   elk
salmon   moose

Directions Complete each sentence using the plural form of the word in parentheses.

1. Dad read the _____ a story.   (child)

2. The story was about two _____ who visit a farm.   (mouse)

3. The mice met two _____.   (goose)

4. The geese had very big _____.   (foot)

5. Their feet looked like large _____ to the mice.   (aircraft)

6. The mice ran away and bumped into some _____.   (sheep)

7. The sheep showed their _____ to the mice.   (tooth)

8. Then the mice saw two _____ grazing by a river.   (oxen)

9. They rode some _____ across the river to get home. (trout)

115

Directions Write the plural form of each word.

1. igloo _____
2. mouse _____
3. fox _____
4. story _____
5. wolf _____
6. elk _____
7. goose _____
8. trout _____
9. fish _____
10. ox _____
11. tray _____
12. knife _____
13. foot _____
14. class _____

Directions Fill in the circle under the word that is the correct plural form of the word that completes the sentence.

1. The fourth grade ____ visited the zoo.
   classes ○   classs ○

2. They saw several ____ in cages.
   foxs ○   foxes ○

3. One group went to see the ____.
   rhinoes ○   rhinos ○

4. Another group saw five ____ grazing.
   elk ○   elks ○

5. A guide showed them where the ____ were.
   wolfs ○   wolves ○

6. The class saw three big ____.
   fishes ○   fish ○

7. Two of the fish were ____.
   trout ○   trouts ○

8. One child saw four ____ running loose.
   gooses ○   geese ○

9. Another saw two white ____ in some hay.
   mice ○   mouses ○

10. Everyone agreed that the ____ were the best.
    kangarooes ○   kangaroos ○

LESSON 58: Test: Plural forms

Name _____

Rule The possessive form of a word is used to show that a person or animal owns, has, or possesses something. To make a singular noun show possession, add **'s** at the end of the word.

EXAMPLES

Joan**'s** skirt
the baby**'s** bottle
the horse**'s** tail

Directions Read each sentence. Circle the word that correctly completes the sentence, and write it on the line.

1. Gerbils are the _____ favorite pets. (classes, class's)

2. The _____ favorite is the hamster. (teachers, teacher's)

3. The _____ fur is thick and soft. (hamsters, hamster's)

4. _____ have fur that is fuzzy. (Gerbils, Gerbil's)

5. The _____ active time can be day or night. (animals, animal's)

6. Their _____ are made of glass. (cages, cage's)

7. They spend hours on their _____. (wheels, wheel's)

Directions Write the possessive form for each word below.

1. boy _____   2. nurse _____

3. girl _____   4. chicken _____

5. friend _____   6. Leslie _____

7. dancer _____   8. man _____

117

Rule When a plural noun ends in **s**, usually just add an apostrophe to show possession. Generally when you see **s'** it tells you that more than one person or animal owns, has, or possesses something.

the boy**s'** books
the dog**s'** houses
the babie**s'** toys

Directions Read each group of words. If the words show that more than one person or thing has something, write **more than one** on the line. If the words show that only one person or thing has something, write **one**.

1. the lumberjack's coat _____

2. the chefs' convention _____

3. the kangaroo's ears _____

4. the woman's hand _____

5. the mothers' march _____

6. the ladies' coats _____

7. the fish's fins _____

8. the clowns' act _____

9. the hero's welcome _____

10. the boys' bikes _____

11. the babies' bibs _____

12. the general's office _____

13. the pianists' contest _____

14. the giraffe's neck _____

15. the orioles' songs _____

16. the hunters' caps _____

LESSON 59: Using the apostrophe to indicate possession

Name _____

children's	porcupine's	eels'	giraffe's
teacher's	world's	bear's	squids'
judges'	ostrich's	birds'	dolphins'

1. The _____ science projects are due today.

2. One _____ class reported on science facts.

3. The _____ largest desert is the Sahara.

4. A _____ long neck is used for fighting.

5. A polar _____ heart beat slows when hibernating.

6. Some _____ eyes are the size of soccer balls.

7. The largest _____ wing feathers are small and useless.

8. Cuckoos lay their eggs in other _____ nests.

9. The _____ tails work like ships' propellers.

10. The _____ electricity helps them find food.

11. A _____ quills measure up to five inches long.

12. The _____ decisions on the winners will be final.

Directions Write the words from the box at the top of the page under the correct heading.

Singular Possessives	**Plural Possessives**
_____	_____
_____	_____
_____	_____
_____	_____
_____	_____
_____	_____

LESSON 60: Apostrophe indicating possession

Directions Read the sentence in each box, and draw a picture to show what the sentence means. Then circle the word or words in each sentence that show possession.

1. A poor peasant borrows his neighbor's sleigh.

2. Tomás's shirt and the girls' blouses are the color of turquoise.

3. Two persons' shawls and someone's feathered hat hung in the closet.

4. The girls' heads were adorned with wreaths made from flower petals and birds' feathers.

LESSON 60: Using the apostrophe to indicate possession

Name _____

Definition A **contraction** is a short way of writing two words. The two words are written together, but one or more letters are left out. An apostrophe stands for missing letters.

EXAMPLES

I am = **I'm**
it is = **it's**
can not = **can't**

Directions In the first column, write the two words the contraction stands for. In the second column, write the letter or letters left out of the contraction.

Words	Letter or Letters Left Out
1. haven't _____	_____
2. isn't _____	_____
3. we've _____	_____
4. you're _____	_____
5. they'll _____	_____

Directions Underline the contraction in each sentence, and write the two words it stands for on the line.

1. We're reading a book about beavers. _____

2. We haven't read about beavers before. _____

3. They're very interesting animals. _____

4. A beaver's tail isn't useless. _____

5. It's shaped like a canoe paddle. _____

Directions   Read the words and write the contraction on the line.

1. can not   _____
2. I am   _____
3. was not   _____
4. he will   _____
5. will not   _____
6. you will   _____
7. could not   _____
8. it is   _____
9. do not   _____
10. are not   _____
11. they have   _____
12. where is   _____

Directions   Read each sentence. Underline the words which can form a contraction. Write the contraction on the line beside the sentence.

1. What is a cloud?   _____
2. Let us think about clouds.   _____
3. Clouds are not marshmallows or cotton.   _____
4. They are drops of water.   _____
5. That is true about clouds.   _____
6. It is hard to believe this about clouds.   _____
7. Clouds will not always bring rain.   _____
8. They will sometimes bring snow or sleet.   _____
9. A cloud can not move without wind.   _____
10. I have learned a little about clouds.   _____

LESSON 61: Contractions

Name _____

1. The funny car doesn't run.

2. The clown's shoes won't fit Sally.

3. The puppy's ears are very long.

4. The elephants' trunks aren't tied together.

5. The flowers don't fit in the vase.

6. The kites' tails are stuck up in the tree.

7. Dave didn't carry the eggs carefully.

8. The birds' nests are in the tree.

_____

_____   _____   _____

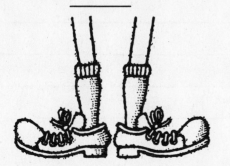      

_____   _____   _____

Directions Read each sentence and underline each word that is a contraction or a possessive. Write each underlined word in the correct box at the bottom of the page. Then choose a sentence and draw a picture to go with it.

1. We're going riding in a hot air balloon.

2. The balloon's colors are green and white.

3. The vessel's name is "Wind Rider."

4. The owner won't let us go up alone.

5. She'll steer the balloon.

6. The owner's crew will help.

7. They'll get the balloon ready.

8. It shouldn't take them long.

9. The crew doesn't need our help.

10. The crew's motto is "Always Ready."

11. The balloon takes off from the farmer's field.

12. It will land on the city's parking lot.

13. A crowd's cheers will greet us as we land.

14. We'll all enjoy this exciting adventure!

CONTRACTIONS	POSSESSIVES
_____	_____
_____	_____
_____	_____
_____	_____
_____	_____
_____	_____
_____	_____

LESSON 62: Test: Uses of the apostrophe

Name _____

Directions Say each word. Write the number of vowels you see in each word. Then write the number of vowel sounds you hear in each word.

	Vowels Seen	Heard			Vowels Seen	Heard
1. bushes	___	___	18. surveys	___	___
2. mysteries	___	___	19. halves	___	___
3. heroes	___	___	20. beliefs	___	___
4. glasses	___	___	21. teeth	___	___
5. tomatoes	___	___	22. waltzes	___	___
6. thieves	___	___	23. pianos	___	___
7. daughters	___	___	24. melodies	___	___
8. foxes	___	___	25. solos	___	___
9. geese	___	___	26. potatoes	___	___
10. injuries	___	___	27. boxes	___	___
11. sombreros	___	___	28. clowns	___	___
12. guesses	___	___	29. leaves	___	___
13. sopranos	___	___	30. activities	___	___
14. shelves	___	___	31. buzzes	___	___
15. cookies	___	___	32. lassos	___	___
16. wives	___	___	33. elves	___	___
17. scratches	___	___	34. patches	___	___

LESSON 63: Syllables

Directions Study Rules 5, 6, and 7 below. On the first line after each word, write the number of the rule that is used in dividing the word into syllables. On the second line, divide the word into syllables using hyphens.

Rule 5 When two or more consonants come between two vowels in a word, the word is usually divided between the first two consonants.

EXAMPLES

hun-gry   bet-ter
suf-fer   pic-ture

Rule 6 When a single consonant comes between two vowels in a word, the word is usually divided after the consonant if the first vowel is short.

EXAMPLES

clev-er   lem-on
rob-in   trav-el

Rule 7 When a single consonant comes between two vowels in a word, the word is usually divided before the consonant if the first vowel is long.

EXAMPLES

mu-sic   po-lar
pa-per   lo-cate

1. circus _____ _____
2. odor _____ _____
3. carton _____ _____
4. habit _____ _____
5. label _____ _____
6. modern _____ _____
7. plenty _____ _____
8. silent _____ _____
9. olive _____ _____
10. tender _____ _____
11. legal _____ _____

12. donate _____ _____
13. punish _____ _____
14. tarnish _____ _____
15. vacant _____ _____
16. medal _____ _____
17. photo _____ _____
18. velvet _____ _____
19. frozen _____ _____
20. lizard _____ _____
21. publish _____ _____
22. radish _____ _____

LESSON 63: Reviewing syllabication rules 5, 6, and 7

Name _____

Definitions A **base word** is a word to which a prefix or suffix may be added to form a new word. A **prefix** is a word part that is added at the beginning of a base word to change the base word's meaning or form a new word.

EXAMPLES

Un, **dis**, and **non** are prefixes that usually mean *not*.

unearned

distrust

nonprofit

Directions Circle the prefix in each word.

1. nonpartisan   2. unkind   3. undress   4. nonessential
5. nonrestrictive   6. discover   7. disappear   8. disinterested
9. nonproductive   10. disclose   11. unclear   12. nonstop
13. nonsense   14. unfold   15. dislike   16. unopened

Directions Complete the unfinished word in each sentence by adding a prefix to the base word in parentheses.

1. These books are _____ to me.   (familiar)
2. I like reading _____ books.   (fiction)
3. I can read a book _____ if it's good.   (stop)
4. I don't _____ reading any kind of book.   (like)
5. Reading is never _____ for me.   (pleasant)

127

Rule The prefixes **ir** and **il** mean *not*.

EXAMPLES
ir + regular = **irregular** (not regular)
il + legal = **illegal** (not legal)

Directions Read each word and circle the prefix.

1. irremovable
2. irrational
3. irrelevant
4. illiterate
5. illogical
6. illegible
7. irresponsible
8. irresistible
9. irreversible

Directions Read the sentences below. Use the information in each sentence to help you write the meaning of the word in boldface print.

1. An argument that is logical makes sense. What is an **illogical** argument?

_____

_____

2. Something that is relevant has to do with the subject being discussed. What is something that is **irrelevant?**

_____

_____

3. If a person's writing is legible, it is easy to read. What is **illegible** writing?

_____

_____

4. A person who is literate is able to read and write. What is an **illiterate** person?

_____

_____

5. A person who is responsible can be depended upon and shows a strong sense of duty. What is an **irresponsible** person?

_____

_____

LESSON 64: Prefixes IR-, IL-

Name _____

Rule The prefixes **im** and **in** can also mean not. The prefixes **em** and **en** mean cause to be or to make.

EXAMPLES

im + proper = **improper** (not proper)
in + curable = **incurable** (not curable)

em + power = **empower** (to make powerful)
en + tangle = **entangle** (to make tangled)

Directions Read the words below. Then circle each prefix.

1. inflexible   2. enlarge   3. impatient   4. embitter

5. encode   6. encase   7. entitled   8. ineffective

9. impossible   10. inaccurately   11. endanger   12. imperfect

Directions Rewrite each sentence below. Use one of the words from above to replace the underlined words.

1. The agent will put the secret message in code.

_____

_____

2. Then the message will not be possible for just anyone to read.

_____

_____

3. We don't want to not accurately encode the message.

_____

_____

129

LESSON 65: Prefixes IN, EN, IM, EM

Making a Difference

It was late summer and Carla was bored. She sat on the front steps, her arms enfolding her knees. She gazed across the street unhappily. "What a misfortune it is to live across from that filthy, unsafe field!" she thought. Bottles and cans littered the ground. Papers blew unchecked around the vacant lot. It was impossible to play baseball or tag or even ride her bike in the rubble. To top it off, the lot was bordered by ugly, unpainted fences.

Carla inhaled deeply, her sigh lost in the sounds of the busy street. Then an idea came to her—an inspiration that hit with the impact of a garbage truck.

Carla gathered all her friends and told them of her plan. None of them disagreed. She emphasized that it was not illegal to gather all the irreparable junk and get it ready for the garbage truck. Once they started, they worked nonstop until everything was done.

Tony picked up all the old bottles. He threw away the broken ones and cashed in the unbroken bottles.

Maria and Carla gathered the aluminum cans and papers from the lot. Then they carried them to the recycling center. The people at the center paid them for their efforts.

"Now let's pool our income," said Carla. Maria added the money, being careful not to miscount it. To everyone's surprise, there was enough money to buy paint for the unsightly fences bordering the vacant lot.

As they completed their painting, the children were surprised to see the local TV reporter from the six o'clock news. That night Carla, Tony, and Maria appeared on the TV news. They talked about their role in turning an unusable lot into an impressive park.

1. Why did Carla think it was a misfortune to live across from the field? _____

_____

2. What word tells you that Carla and her friends worked until the job was

   done? _____

3. What is income? _____

4. If a fence is unsightly, what does it look like? _____

_____

Name _____

Rules **Ex** is a prefix that usually means *out from* or *beyond*. **Re** is a prefix that usually means *again* or *back*. **De** is a prefix that usually means *down from, away from,* or *the opposite of the base word.*

EXAMPLES
ex + port = **export** (to send goods out of a country to another)
re + pay = **repay** (to pay again or to pay back)
de + press = **depress** (to press something)

Directions Circle the prefix in each word.

1. rebuild	2. rejoiced	3. declassify
4. depart	5. demerit	6. refresh
7. retrace	8. exchange	9. research
10. deplanes	11. extends	12. exclaims
13. depressed	14. reapply	15. removes

Directions Complete each sentence with a word from the list above.

1. Sal sits in his seat and waits for the plane to _____.

2. He is going to Mexico to _____ his family tree.

3. After takeoff, the pilot _____, "It's a lovely day to fly."

4. When the plane lands, Sal _____ and enters the airport.

5. First, he must _____ his money for some Mexican money.

6. Then he buys some cold juice to _____ himself.

7. It is too warm outside, so he _____ his coat.

8. Finally, Sal _____ his arm to hail a taxi and is on his way.

131

1. Tell when you might <u>return</u> something to a store.

   _____

   _____

2. Write about a time you wanted to <u>exchange</u> something with a friend.

   _____

   _____

3. Tell what you would do to <u>decode</u> a message.

   _____

   _____

4. Explain how a cook might <u>defrost</u> some frozen meat.

   _____

   _____

5. Tell when someone might <u>rewash</u> a bicycle.

   _____

   _____

6. Write a short news spot telling how the police <u>recaptured</u> a gorilla who escaped from the zoo.

   _____

   _____

7. List three things that can <u>explode</u>.

   _____

   _____

8. Tell two reasons why drivers might have to take a <u>detour</u> instead of their normal route.

   _____

   _____

Name _____

Rule **Co**, **com**, and **con** are prefixes that can mean with or together.

EXAMPLES
co + operate = **cooperate** (to work with others)
com + press = **compress** (to press together)
con + verse = **converse** (to talk with others)

Directions Circle the word that describes each picture.

1.

compose   combat

2.

conductor   convict

3.

compete   combine

4.

conversation   conclude

5.

cosign   copilot

6.

contest   connect

Directions Circle the prefix in each of the following words. Then write a short definition of the word.

1. c o a u t h o r _____

2. c o n j o i n _____

3. c o m p a c t _____

4. c o e x i s t _____

5. c o m p i l e _____

6. c o p i l o t _____

LESSON 67: Prefixes CO-, COM-, CON-

Directions Circle the word that best completes the sentence and write the word on the line.

1. Jackie's scout troop is having a _____ to clean up the local parks.

   contest
   detest

2. They are trying to get everyone in their _____ involved.

   community
   compare

3. On Saturday, Jackie's troop held a meeting to _____ the rules.

   explain
   explode

4. They formed _____ to work together.

   comments
   committees

5. Jackie _____ the steps involved in cleaning up a park.

   described
   deported

6. Everyone at the meeting agreed to _____ in cleaning up the parks.

   coauthor
   cooperate

7. They all hoped the city would _____ some of the broken picnic tables.

   replace
   refill

8. They _____ ideas about what they might do.

   exchanged
   exceeded

9. Before everyone _____, they wished each other luck.

   designed
   departed

LESSON 67: Test: Prefixes EX-, RE-, DE-, CO-, COM-, CON-

Name _____

Rule The prefixes **fore**, **pre**, and **pro** have slightly different meanings.

EXAMPLES
fore + warn = **forewarn** (to warn before something happens)
pre + heat = **preheat** (to heat ahead of time)
pro + ject = **project** (to throw forward)

Directions Circle the prefix in each word.

1. forearm
2. prefix
3. preview
4. propel
5. pronoun
6. forenoon
7. prepare
8. forehead
9. produce
10. forefathers
11. foresight
12. prepay

Directions Fill in the circle beside the word that best completes each sentence.

1. Tanya has ___ that she will someday be a great tennis player.
   ○ prorated   ○ prepaid   ○ proclaimed

2. Every day in practice, she works on her ___ and backhand shots.
   ○ forefather   ○ forehand   ○ project

3. She is working hard to ___ for next month's big city tournament.
   ○ propel   ○ prepare   ○ foresee

4. Today, she must play a ___ match to qualify for the tournament.
   ○ preliminary   ○ prefix   ○ prevention

5. Tanya's coach ___ her that the competition would be stiff.
   ○ produced   ○ forewarned   ○ pretended

6. However, her coach ___ that she will make the tournament.
   ○ predicts   ○ prevents   ○ preserves

135

forecast	protect	professional	presented	produce
preserve	propose	forewarned	promote	pretend
prepay	forearm	forefathers	protest	prepare

Across

2. to guard against harm or danger
3. to prepare food for later use by canning, pickling, or salting
5. to make an offer of marriage
7. a person who works in an occupation that requires special education and training
9. to raise to a higher rank or grade
10. to make believe as in a play
11. to give money ahead of time

Down

1. to tell or try to tell how something will turn out
3. to make something ready before the time that it is needed
4. to get ready for trouble before it comes
6. to speak out against, to object
7. shown
8. advised

LESSON 68: Prefixes FORE, PRE, PRO

Name _____

Rule **Super** and **over** are prefixes that mean over, above, extra, or too much.

EXAMPLES
super + human = **superhuman** (having a nature above human beings)
over + size = **oversize** (greater than normal size)

Directions Circle the prefix in each word.

1. supervisor
2. overtime
3. overjoyed
4. oversleep
5. overcooked
6. supermarket
7. overcoat
8. superwoman
9. overeat

Directions Complete each sentence with a word from the list above.

1. Pat set her alarm clock so she wouldn't _____.

2. She was a _____, so she had to get to work before her employees.

3. Before work, Pat _____ her toast and burned it to a crisp.

4. It was raining so Pat put on her _____ and left for work.

5. Pat would have had to be a _____ to get all her work done.

6. There was so much work that Pat asked her staff to work

_____.

7. On her way home, Pat stopped at the _____ to pick up some food.

8. Pat was _____ when she finally got home after her hard day.

Rules The prefixes **sub** and **under** mean under, below or beneath, or not quite. The prefix **out** means outside, away from, better than, or more than.

EXAMPLES
sub + soil = **subsoil** (soil under the surface layer)
sub + tropical = **subtropical** (not quite tropical)
under + age = **underage** (below the age required)
out + building = **outbuilding** (away from the main building)
out + do = **outdo** (to do better than another)

Directions Read the story. Underline the words that have the prefixes **sub**, **under**, and **out**. Then answer the following questions using as many of the underlined words as you can.

Everyone Can Have a Garden

Steve and Kim live outside the city in a suburban development. A vacant lot has been subdivided into small garden plots. The subsoil is rocky, but the topsoil is good for growing vegetables.

One morning they gathered outside, with all the other gardeners, underneath the sunny sky. Everyone worked together to cut away all the underbrush and clear away the rocks. Soon the vacant lot had undergone an outstanding change.

"It'll be great to have fresh lettuce and tomatoes for submarine sandwiches," said Kim.

There was an outburst of laughter as everyone agreed with Kim.

1. Where do Kim and Steve live? _____

_____

2. Why did everyone laugh when Kim mentioned lettuce and tomatoes? _____

_____

3. What are submarine sandwiches? _____

_____

Name _____

bi + plane = **biplane** (an airplane with two sets of wings)

tri + angle = **triangle** (a figure with three angles)

Directions Read each sentence. Then use the other words in the sentence to help you understand the meaning of the underlined word. Write the meaning of the underlined word on the line.

1. Brad, Glenda, and José have sung together as a trio for a long time.

   A trio is _____.

2. In 1976, they sang at the bicentennial birthday party for the United States.

   Bicentennial means _____.

3. Twice a year, they sing at the biannual state singing festival.

   Biannual means _____.

4. They have special tricolor costumes in red, white, and blue.

   Tricolor means _____

Directions Match each word with its definition and write the number of the word on the line. You may wish to use your dictionary.

1. biennial   _____ happening every two years

2. biped   _____ a vehicle with three wheels

3. tricycle   _____ happening every two months

4. tricentennial   _____ an animal with only two feet

5. trisect   _____ happening every three hundred years

6. bimonthly   _____ to divide into three equal parts

139

EXAMPLES
semi + annual = **semiannual** (every half year)
mid + year = **midyear** (the middle of the year)

Directions Read each word in the box and circle the prefixes *semi* and **mid.** Then read each definition, and write the word from the list that goes with it.

midsummer	midway	semicircle	semitropical	midair
midwinter	midwest	semifinal	midshipman	midterm

1. the time of the year when January comes _____

2. a round or match that comes before the final one in a contest or tournament _____

3. the middle of a school semester _____

4. half of a circle _____

Directions Words beginning with the prefixes **semi** and **mid** are hidden in the puzzle below. Some go across, and others go up and down. Circle each word as you find it in the puzzle. Then write the word under the correct heading.

mid

_____

_____

_____

semi

_____

_____

```
A C E G M I M I D S U M M E R
M O Q S I U W Y A E D F H J L
N P M I D S H I P M A N R T V
X Z A C A Y Z B Q I D W E A T
D F H J I L N P R C T V X Z B
C E T G R M I D W I N T E R L
I K E M Y O G S U R W X Z A C
S E M I T R O P I C A L C E G
F H I J I N P Q S L U W Y A I
K M F N P M I R T E Y M R T Y
```

LESSON 70: Prefixes SEMI-, MID-

Name _____

> **Remember** these rules for dividing words into syllables.

A word has as many syllables as it has vowel sounds.

When a word has a prefix, divide the word between the prefix and the base word. Some prefixes have more than one syllable.

When two or more consonants come between two vowels in a word, the word is usually divided between the first two consonants.

When a single consonant comes between two vowels in a word, the word is usually divided after the consonant if the first vowel is short.

When a single consonant comes between two vowels in a word, the word is usually divided before the consonant if the first vowel is long.

Directions Underline the prefix in each of the following words. On the line, divide the word into syllables using hyphens.

1. semiannual _____

2. superhuman _____

3. overeat _____

4. forewarned _____

5. pronoun _____

6. submarine _____

7. triweekly _____

8. outrage _____

9. prepays _____

10. midday _____

11. biplane _____

12. underwater _____

Directions Write a word from above to complete each sentence.

1. Every other year, Ted's family goes on a _____ vacation.

2. To get to the island they must take a _____.

3. Sometimes they see a _____ that looks like a big whale.

4. At _____, they have lunch on the diving boat.

5. After lunch, the family jumps overboard and dives _____.

141

un	dis	non	ir	il	in	en	im	em	ex
re	de	co	com	con	fore	pre	pro	super	over
sub	under	out	bi	tri	semi	mid			

A Grand Vacation

Last summer our family decided to take an overland trip by train. Riding on an express train was most enjoyable. Besides, we were conserving gas by not driving our car.

The trip to the Grand Canyon included many things that entertained us: scenery to admire, new people to converse with, games to play, and good meals in the dining car. I enjoyed the dining car most of all.

At the Grand Canyon there are many overlooks. At each one we stopped to enjoy the wonderful scenery. It is hard to comprehend the immensity of the canyon. I can't explain it, and I can't describe it. It is beyond description.

From the rim of the canyon, we also had a preview of another train we would take the next day—a mule train. Mule trains and hiking are the two ways you can descend into the canyon. Guides had prepared food and beverages for our descent. They made certain we did not get hurt or fall.

We stayed overnight down in the canyon and returned to the rim the next day. The ascent from the canyon was rugged, and we arrived at the top exhausted. In spite of our exhaustion, we were happy and impressed by it all. We proclaimed our trip the best we had ever undertaken.

1. What did the writer like best about the express train ride? _____

   _____

2. Why didn't the writer describe the Grand Canyon? _____

   _____

3. What word can you think of that could be used instead of saying "beyond description"? _____

4. What kind of train did the writer's family take to reach the bottom of the canyon? _____

5. What does exhausted mean? _____

Name _____

Definition A **root** is a word part to which a prefix or suffix may be added to form a new word.

EXAMPLES

Root	Meaning	Example
pos	place	**pos**ition
pel	push	pro**pel**

Directions Read the following words. Circle each word that has the root **pos**. Underline each word that contains **pel**.

1. posed
2. expel
3. impose
4. dispose
5. compose
6. repellent
7. compel
8. dispel
9. repose

Directions Read each sentence. Circle the meaning of the underlined word.

1. Nan's mom expelled Nan's cat from the kitchen for jumping on the table.

   a. to forcefully remove   **b.** to politely excuse

2. She proposed that the cat be banned from the kitchen at mealtimes.

   a. to suggest   **b.** to invite

3. Nan agreed and promised that the cat would not impose on her again.

   a. to help   **b.** to bother

4. With the cat problem dispelled, Nan could get back to her homework.

   a. to surround   **b.** to make disappear

143

LESSON 72: Roots POS, PEL

Hint Here are some roots, or word parts, that appear in many English words.

EXAMPLES		
Root	**Meaning**	**Example**
port	carry	**port**able
ject	throw	re**ject**

Directions Circle the root in each of the following words.

1. import
2. rejection
3. projectile
4. eject
5. porter
6. report
7. injection
8. project
9. transportation

Directions Choose the word that best completes each sentence and write the word on the line.

1. Our class is working on a _____ about international trade.

   project
   important

2. Each year, our country _____ many products from other countries.

   objects
   imports

3. For example, our movie _____ at school was made in Japan.

   projector
   portion

4. Many _____ televisions are also made in other countries.

   rejection
   portable

5. The products are _____ across the ocean in large ships.

   transported
   ejection

Name _____

EXAMPLES

Root	Meaning	Example
duct	lead	con**duct**
duce	lead	in**duce**
tract	pull or draw	dis**tract**

Directions Read each sentence. Underline each word that has the root **duct**, **duce**, or **tract** and write the meaning of the word on the line.

1. Sam needed to finish his homework but was distracted by loud music.

   _____

   _____

2. He found his brother in the garage conducting his rock-and-roll band.

   _____

   _____

3. The band had signed a contract to play at a school dance on Saturday.

   _____

   _____

4. Sam asked if they could reduce the noise level so he could study.

   _____

   _____

Directions Read the words and the definitions. Write the number of each word on the line beside its definition.

1. deduct   ____ to bring into view

2. conductor   ____ to take or pull back

3. produce   ____ to subtract or take away from

4. tractor   ____ person who leads

5. retract   ____ machine used for pulling

Hint Look at these roots, or word parts, and study their meanings.	**EXAMPLES**		
	Root	**Meaning**	**Example**
	spec	see, look, examine	spec**ify**
	spect	see, look, examine	in**spect**
	scribe	write	in**scribe**

Directions Circle the word that describes each picture.

1.

spectator   spectacular

2.
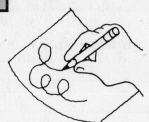

subscribe   scribble

3.

inspector   prospector

4.

describe   subscription

5.

respects   inspects

6.
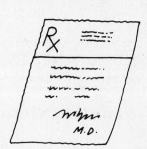

prescription   description

Directions Write the number of each word on the line beside its definition.

1. inspector   ____ one who watches rather than takes part in an event

2. description   ____ something written, as on a coin or in a book

3. spectator   ____ one who looks for profit

4. prescription   ____ one who looks for clues or evidence

5. inscription   ____ something written by a doctor

6. speculator   ____ telling about in detail

LESSON 73: Roots SPEC, SPECT, SCRIBE

Name _____

EXAMPLES

Root	Meaning	Root	Meaning
pos	place	ject	throw
pel	push	tract	pull or draw
duce, duct	lead	scribe	write
port	carry	spec, spect	see or look

Directions Review the roots and their meanings listed above. Then divide the words below into prefixes and roots. Use a plus sign to separate the two parts. Example: im + port

1. report _____
2. compel _____
3. deduct _____
4. prescribe _____
5. respect _____
6. reduce _____
7. subject _____
8. extract _____
9. inject _____
10. dispose _____

Directions Complete each sentence with a word from the list above.

1. Jon's mom calls the doctor to _____ his symptoms.

2. The doctor tells her how to _____ Jon's high fever.

3. He also wants to _____ some pills for Jon.

4. Jon doesn't want the doctor to _____ any medicine with a needle.

5. The doctor says he will _____ Jon's wishes for now.

6. That night at dinner Jon's health was the _____ of discussion.

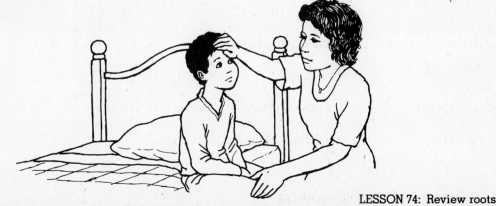

Directions Circle the meaning of each root.

1. **pos**	throw / send / place	2. **ject**	say / throw / pull	3. **pel**	push / pull / turn	4. **tract**	carry / place / pull
5. **port**	say / carry / write	6. **scribe**	see / write / lead	7. **duce** or **duct**	pull / throw / lead	8. **spec** or **spect**	pull / write / see, look

Directions Read each clue. Find the word in the list that matches the clue. Then write the answer word in the crossword puzzle. You may need to check your dictionary.

invisible	research	semimonthly	conclusion
projectile	conducted	disprove	described

Across

3. to show that something is false or incorrect

5. not able to be seen

7. happening twice a month

8. told or written about in detail

Down

1. an object made to be shot with force through the air

2. careful, patient study to find out facts and principles

4. an opinion reached by thinking; judgment

6. led or guided

LESSON 74: Test: Prefixes and roots

Name _____

Directions Read each word. Write the number of vowels you see in each word. Then write the number of vowel sounds you hear.

	Vowels	
	Seen	**Heard**
1. discomfort	_____	_____
2. supermarket	_____	_____
3. demerit	_____	_____
4. triangle	_____	_____
5. overseas	_____	_____
6. nonresident	_____	_____
7. outcast	_____	_____
8. explode	_____	_____
9. uncertain	_____	_____
10. preview	_____	_____
11. retract	_____	_____
12. inspection	_____	_____
13. underweight	_____	_____
14. combine	_____	_____
15. irregular	_____	_____
16. repellent	_____	_____
17. semicircle	_____	_____

	Vowels	
	Seen	**Heard**
18. inscription	_____	_____
19. pronoun	_____	_____
20. enclose	_____	_____
21. bicycle	_____	_____
22. forenoon	_____	_____
23. disappear	_____	_____
24. midnight	_____	_____
25. recover	_____	_____
26. contestant	_____	_____
27. illegal	_____	_____
28. objection	_____	_____
29. embitter	_____	_____
30. submarine	_____	_____
31. unhealthy	_____	_____
32. portable	_____	_____
33. coexist	_____	_____
34. depress	_____	_____

con-duct   su-per-vise
re-port   o-ver-night

Directions Read each word. Divide it into syllables, using hyphens.

1. reject _____
2. irritate _____
3. conduct _____
4. employ _____
5. nonfiction _____
6. import _____
7. produce _____
8. induce _____
9. prescribe _____
10. unclean _____
11. compose _____
12. retract _____
13. illegal _____
14. repel _____
15. description _____
16. underground _____

17. induct _____
18. important _____
19. biplane _____
20. distract _____
21. compel _____
22. enclose _____
23. expect _____
24. irregular _____
25. subject _____
26. inject _____
27. inspect _____
28. deduce _____
29. propel _____
30. nonsense _____
31. superhero _____
32. inscribe _____

Name _____

Definition **Synonyms** are words that have the same or almost the same meaning.

EXAMPLES

sad—unhappy   glad—happy

Directions Draw a line to connect each pair of synonyms.

1.

journey	hurry
hasten	direct
worried	trip
straight	anxious

2.

raw	belief
discover	secure
safe	find
faith	uncooked

3.

hurt	ask
question	injure
examine	destroy
ruin	inspect

Directions Complete the story by writing a synonym from the box for each word in parentheses.

| bathes | frequently | every | shines | loves | like |
| town | acting | quickly | nourishes | receives | saving |

Carl _____ his dog Muffin. He walks Muffin along
(adores)

_____ streets _____ day. He
(city)   (each)

_____ him well and _____ brushes his silky
(feeds)   (often)

coat until it _____. Sometimes he _____
(glistens)   (washes)

him, but Muffin does not _____ that.
(enjoy)

When Muffin _____ a bone for _____
(gets)   (behaving)

well, he _____ buries it with others that he is
(promptly)

_____.
(keeping)

LESSON 76: Synonyms

1.	**walk**	stroll	saunter	trudge	tumble	march
2.	**cold**	chilly	creep	cool	icy	freezing
3.	**hot**	warm	heated	joyful	boiling	roasted
4.	**quick**	swift	fast	rapid	gloomy	speedy
5.	**strong**	powerful	lengthy	hardy	vigorous	forceful
6.	**weak**	happy	frail	feeble	fragile	sickly

Directions Unscramble the letters in each box to find a synonym for the word.

1.

heir	simot	dubot	varbe	recof	pealse

damp   m _ _ _ _   compel   f _ _ _ _

mistrust   d _ _ _ _ _   courageous   b _ _ _ _

employ   h _ _ _   satisfy   p _ _ _ _ _

2.

perec	pdira	raleg	pphay	akblc	alsml

ebony   b _ _ _ _   crawl   c _ _ _ _

swift   r _ _ _ _   little   s _ _ _ _

content   h _ _ _ _   huge   l _ _ _ _

Name _____

Definition **Antonyms** are words that are opposite or almost opposite in meaning.

Examples

happy—sad   large—small

Directions   Circle the words in each row that are antonyms of the word in the box.

1.	slow	quick	happy	fast	rapid	swift
2.	sweet	sour	tart	bitter	sugary	unsweet
3.	weak	strong	hardy	powerless	powerful	forceful
4.	safe	secure	uncertain	insecure	unsafe	unprotected
5.	forbid	allow	refuse	permit	tolerate	approve
6.	distrust	trust	faith	belief	disbelief	confidence

Directions   Find the word in the first sentence in each pair that is an antonym of a word in the second sentence. Underline the two words.

1.   Roy had just started skating and found it difficult.
2.   Ted had been skating for years and made it look easy.

3.   Ted felt that Roy was getting much better at skating.
4.   Every time Roy fell, he felt he was just getting worse.

5.   Roy and Ted ice skated until they became chilly.
6.   Then they went indoors to get warm.

tasty	quiet	joyful	follow
narrow	frown	hard	fresh

1. soft ____ ____ ____ ____   2. bland ____ ____ ____ ____

3. noisy ____ ____ ____ ____   4. wide ____ ____ ____ ____

5. smile ____ ____ ____ ____   6. unhappy ____ ____ ____ ____

7. stale ____ ____ ____ ____   8. lead ____ ____ ____ ____

Directions Read each sentence and the pair of words that follows. Choose the word that best completes the sentence and write the word on the line.

1. For the first time, the usually honest boy

   was _____ about his behavior.

   untruthful

   truthful

2. He said he would take the fastest way home,

   but he took the _____.

   quickest

   slowest

3. His mother was unhappy with him but

   _____ to see he was safe.

   disappointed

   overjoyed

4. The hungry boy devoured his food and was

   soon _____.

   full

   empty

5. Then he took off his dirty clothes and put on

   some _____ pajamas.

   soiled

   clean

6. Feeling tired, he went to bed so he would

   be _____ the next day.

   rested

   exhausted

Name _____

Definition	EXAMPLES
Homonyms are words that sound alike but have different meanings and usually different spellings.	to—two—too no—know

Directions   Read each pair of sentences. Write the words that sound alike on the lines.

1.   Bud was walking through the produce department. _____

2.   Joe threw an apple to Bud. _____

---

3.   "Which way are you going?" asked Joe. _____

4.   "Would you weigh this apple for me?" _____

---

5.   "It weighs two ounces," said Bud. _____

6.   "Toss it back to me," said Joe. _____

Directions   In each set, draw a line from each word in the first column to its homonym in the second column.

1.		**2.**		**3.**	
steal	see	dear	pale	hair	urn
meet	steel	cheap	deer	blue	blew
sea	meat	pail	cheep	earn	hare

1. gait
   gate

2. eight
   ate

3. meet
   meat

4. bread
   bred

5. horse
   hoarse

6. peal
   peel

7. dear
   deer

8. knight
   night

9. would
   wood

Directions Write the word on the line that best completes each sentence.

1. Our _____, Mrs. Fox, visited our class.

   principle
   principal

2. Our class read _____ for her.

   aloud
   allowed

3. Then we showed her how well we can _____.

   right
   write

4. Our math homework was _____ today.

   due
   dew

5. The problems were _____ very hard.

   knot
   not

6. We _____ Mrs. Fox was proud of us.

   know
   no

7. She told us _____ keep up the good work.

   two
   to

Name _____

> **Directions** Read each sentence. Write a short definition for each underlined word.

1. We can't tell <u>whether</u> or not the <u>weather</u> will improve.

   whether _____

   weather _____

2. If the weather improves, we will go to <u>see</u> the <u>sea</u> lions at the marina.

   see _____

   sea _____

3. On our <u>way</u> to the marina, we guess how much a sea lion might <u>weigh</u>.

   way _____

   weigh _____

4. We <u>peer</u> at them as they sit on the <u>pier</u>.

   peer _____

   pier _____

5. Maybe rain will <u>pour</u> down on the <u>poor</u> sea lions.

   pour _____

   poor _____

6. I wish I <u>knew</u> if the <u>new</u> forecast calls for rain.

   knew _____

   new _____

Definition **Homonyms** are words that sound alike but have different meanings and usually different spellings.

1. Ann had only <u>four</u> days to prepare <u>for</u> the big race.

   _____ because of

   _____ the number between three and five

2. She <u>knew</u> that a <u>new</u> sail would make her go faster.

   _____ was certain

   _____ never before used

3. Ann bought a new <u>sail</u> for her boat at the clearance <u>sale</u>.

   _____ an event where prices are reduced

   _____ a sheet of material used to catch wind

4. The wind <u>blew</u> and filled the pretty <u>blue</u> sail.

   _____ the color of the sky on a clear day

   _____ did blow

5. Ann was never <u>bored</u> on <u>board</u> her sailboat.

   _____ uninterested

   _____ on a boat, airplane, or bus

Name _____

Directions Read each sentence. Decide whether the two underlined words are synonyms, antonyms, or homonyms. Fill in the circle beside your choice.

Definitions **Synonyms** are words that are alike or almost alike in meaning. **Antonyms** are words that are opposite or almost opposite in meaning. **Homonyms** are words that sound alike but have different meanings and usually different spellings.

1. Tina <u>read</u> a book called *The <u>Red</u> Shawl* for school.
   ○ synonyms   ○ antonyms   ○ homonyms

2. It was about an <u>old</u> woman and her <u>young</u> granddaughter.
   ○ synonyms   ○ antonyms   ○ homonyms

3. They <u>would</u> always sit on the <u>wood</u> porch swing and talk.
   ○ synonyms   ○ antonyms   ○ homonyms

4. Grandma told <u>amazing</u> stories of her <u>wonderful</u> life.
   ○ synonyms   ○ antonyms   ○ homonyms

5. Some stories made the girl <u>laugh</u> so hard that she would <u>cry</u>.
   ○ synonyms   ○ antonyms   ○ homonyms

6. Whether it was <u>warm</u> or <u>cold</u>, Grandma always wore her red shawl.
   ○ synonyms   ○ antonyms   ○ homonyms

7. The <u>pretty</u> red shawl always made Grandma feel <u>beautiful</u>.
   ○ synonyms   ○ antonyms   ○ homonyms

8. One day, Grandma gave the <u>big</u> red shawl to the <u>little</u> girl.
   ○ synonyms   ○ antonyms   ○ homonyms

9. The <u>excited</u> child was <u>thrilled</u> to receive it!
   ○ synonyms   ○ antonyms   ○ homonyms

10. Grandma <u>knew</u> it would be taken care of by its <u>new</u> owner.
    ○ synonyms   ○ antonyms   ○ homonyms

159

Directions Read each pair of words. Write an **S** on the line if they are **synonyms**. Write an **A** if they are **antonyms**. Write and **H** if they are **homonyms**.

1. walk—stroll _____
2. moist—damp _____
3. so—sew _____
4. rapid—speedy _____
5. son—sun _____
6. weak—feeble _____
7. great—grate _____
8. crooked—straight _____
9. write—right _____
10. stingy—generous _____
11. behavior—conduct _____
12. compel—force _____
13. insecure—safe _____
14. sight—site _____
15. foolish—unwise _____
16. whether—weather _____
17. flawless—imperfect _____
18. buy—by _____
19. through—threw _____
20. distrust—belief _____
21. peace—piece _____
22. lucky—unfortunate _____
23. sense—nonsense _____
24. principal—principle _____

25. cold—chilly _____
26. healthy—sickly _____
27. your—you're _____
28. darkness—daylight _____
29. strong—powerful _____
30. sell—cell _____
31. unhappy—joyful _____
32. quiet—noisy _____
33. eight—ate _____
34. lovely—attractive _____
35. legal—illegal _____
36. fearful—brave _____
37. knight—night _____
38. incomplete—unfinished _____
39. slowly—quickly _____
40. rain—reign _____
41. whole—entire _____
42. inspect—examine _____
43. allow—forbid _____
44. piece—fragment _____
45. injure—hurt _____
46. immature—childish _____
47. allowed—aloud _____
48. tasteless—tasty _____

LESSON 80: Test: Synonyms, antonyms, homonyms

Name _____

Hint Words in a dictionary are arranged in alphabetical order. When words begin with the same letter or letters, look at the second or third letter to put the words in alphabetical order.

EXAMPLES

j**a**y	ju**d**ge
j**e**an	ju**g**
j**o**g	ju**i**ce

Directions Number the words in each group to show the alphabetical order.

1.
pearl _____
pin _____
powder _____
part _____
photo _____

2.
door _____
duty _____
date _____
drain _____
digest _____

3.
llama _____
lucky _____
lodge _____
lying _____
lizard _____

Directions Write the names of these animals in alphabetical order. Use the dictionary to find out about the animals you do not know.

dolphin	deer	lion	leopard	monkey	mouse
dodo	donkey	llama	lynx	mule	mink

_____   _____   _____

_____   _____   _____

_____   _____   _____

_____   _____   _____

161

LESSON 81: Alphabetical order

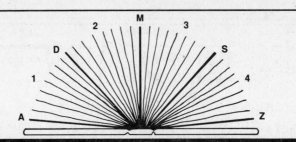

Dictionary tip
The words in a dictionary are listed in alphabetical order from **A** to **Z**.

Directions Read each word and figure out in which section of the dictionary you would find this word. Use the picture at the top of the page to help you. Then write the word <u>first</u>, <u>second</u>, <u>third</u>, or <u>fourth</u> on the line next to each word.

1. banquet _____

2. imposter _____

3. frontier _____

4. turret _____

5. privilege _____

6. repeal _____

Directions See how quickly you can find these words in the dictionary. Then write each word on the line beside its definition.

jerkin	barnacle	petunia
abacus	redwood	easel

1. used for doing math quickly without writing _____

2. a standing frame for holding an artist's painting _____

3. a short, tight jacket often without sleeves _____

4. a plant with flowers of various colors

_____

5. a giant evergreen tree found in California and Oregon _____

6. a small sea animal with a shell which fastens itself to rocks and the bottoms of boats _____

LESSON 81: Locating words in the dictionary

Name _____

Directions Look at each pair of guide words and the words below them. Cross out any words that would **not** be found on the same page as those guide words. Then write the remaining words in alphabetical order on the lines.

Definition Guide words are found at the top of each dictionary page. The guide words tell you the first and last word on each page. The remaining words on the dictionary page are in alphabetical order between the two guide words.

1. fluffy/fold

fly _____

foil _____

foot _____

focus _____

2. muddle/napkin

nap _____

much _____

mystery _____

nation _____

3. safety/sauce

salad _____

satisfy _____

salt _____

sad _____

4. oar/oft

object _____

oak _____

occur _____

out _____

5. penny/pizza

plain _____

people _____

piano _____

perfect _____

6. job/jug

jog _____

jut _____

jolt _____

join _____

Directions Look at each pair of guide words. Circle the words that would be on the same dictionary page as the guide words. Then number the circled words in each column in alphabetical order.

1. ant/apple

_____ apart

_____ apt

_____ apologize

2. dose/drake

_____ down

_____ doze

_____ dot

3. machine/make

_____ major

_____ male

_____ magazine

Directions Read the words in the box. Then read the pairs of guide words below. Find three words in the box that would be on the dictionary page with each pair of guide words. Write those words in alphabetical order on the lines beneath the guide words.

osprey	rasp	moat	mirror	mixer	ornament
moist	ours	ought	rake	raft	ram

1. **mineral/model**

_____

_____

_____

2. **organ/ounce**

_____

_____

_____

3. **radio/rank**

_____

_____

_____

Directions Read the information in each exercise. Decide whether the word would appear **before, on,** or **after** the dictionary page with those guide words. Write your answer on the line.

1. You open the dictionary and see the guide words **firm/fixture.**
   Would the word **fist** come <u>before</u>, <u>on</u>, or <u>after</u> this dictionary page?   _____

2. You open the dictionary and see the guide words **grief/grotto.**
   Would the word **grew** come <u>before</u>, <u>on</u>, or <u>after</u> this dictionary page?   _____

3. You open the dictionary and see the guide words **swell/swine.**
   Would the word **sword** come <u>before</u>, <u>on</u>, or <u>after</u> this dictionary page?   _____

LESSON 82: Dictionary guide words

Name _____

Dictionary tip
The words shown in boldface print in the dictionary are called **entry words**. All the information about an entry word is called an **entry**.

MORE DICTIONARY TIPS
Many words that begin with **un-**, **re-**, or **dis-** or end with **s**, **es**, **ing**, **ed**, **er**, or **est** are not listed as separate entry words in the dictionary. To find the meaning of these words, look up the base word to which the prefix or ending has been added.

Abbreviations and contractions are listed alphabetically in the dictionary as though they are whole words.

Directions Read each word. Then write the entry word you would look up in the dictionary. Remember that if a word has a common prefix or suffix, you may need to look up the base word to which the prefix or suffix has been added.

1. clouds _____
3. wider _____
5. poodles _____
7. racing _____
9. knitting _____
11. angriest _____
13. permitted _____
15. rewrap _____

2. corrected _____
4. darkness _____
6. ivies _____
8. omitting _____
10. rained _____
12. pennies _____
14. repack _____
16. dryly _____

Directions For each group, number the abbreviations and contractions in alphabetical order. Then write the word or phrase each stands for.

____ M.D. _____
____ lb. _____
____ km _____
____ CA _____
____ Fri. _____

____ can't _____
____ they'll _____
____ who's _____
____ here's _____
____ we've _____

Directions Read the dictionary meanings. Then write the number of the meaning of each underlined word in the sentences below.

Hint Many entries in the dictionary list more than one meaning for an entry word.

1. **date** 1 the time at which a thing happens. 2 the day of the month. 3 the words or figures on a coin or letter that tell when it was made.

____ Marla needs a penny with the date 1964 to complete her coin collection.

____ The date of Martin Luther King's birth was January 15, 1929.

2. **glaring** 1 shining so brightly as to hurt the eyes. 2 too bright and showy. 3 staring at in an angry way. 4 standing out so that it cannot be overlooked.

____ I do not like the glaring color of those bright pink and green socks.

____ The glaring headlights hurt Mr. Day's eyes.

____ The accountant found a glaring mistake in the company records.

3. **save** 1 to rescue or keep from harm or danger. 2 to keep or store up for future use. 3 to keep from being lost or wasted. 4 to keep from being worn out or damaged.

____ Jill plans to save her best shoes for special parties.

____ Paco was able to save his dog from drowning.

____ The squirrels save nuts and seeds so they will have food to eat during the winter.

4. **instrument** 1 a person or thing used to get something done. 2 a tool for doing exact work. 3 a device used in making musical sounds. 4 a legal paper by means of which some action is carried out.

____ My sister plays an instrument in the school band.

____ A lawyer can prepare a legal instrument such as a deed or will.

____ A dentist uses a special instrument to clean teeth.

LESSON 83: Selecting the correct entry word meaning

Name _____

beyond **1** on the far side of; farther away than. **2** later than. **3** outside the reach or power of. **4** more or better than.

edge **1** the sharp, cutting part. **2** the line or part where something ends. **3** the brink.

favor **1** a helpful or kind action. **2** liking or approval. **3** a small souvenir.

groove **1** a long and narrow hollow, cut or worn in a surface. **2** the track cut in a phonograph record for the needle to follow. **3** a regular way of doing something as by habit.

hutch **1** a pen or coop for small animals. **2** a chest for storing things. **3** a china cabinet with open shelves on top.

level **1** with no part higher than any other part; flat and even. **2** as high as something else. **3** not excited or confused.

paw **1** to touch, dig, or hit with the paws or feet. **2** to handle in a rough and clumsy way.

range **1** a row or line of connected mountains. **2** open land over which cattle graze. **3** a cooking stove.

1. Dad was hanging a picture by the _____ in the dining room.

2. He asked Dan to do him a _____ and get a hammer.

3. There was a hammer in the kitchen by the _____.

4. Before Dad hung the picture, he asked Dan if it was _____.

5. Dan set the hammer near the _____ of the table, and it fell.

6. Dad tried to pick it up, but it was _____ his reach.

Directions Read the list of homographs and their meanings. Then decide which words to use to complete Jamie's story. Write the words and their numbers on the lines below the story.

Definition Homographs are words that are spelled alike, but have different meanings. In the dictionary, entry words that are homographs have a small raised number to the right of the word.

clip[1] to cut off or cut out with scissors.
clip[2] to fasten things together.
firm[1] that stays the same; not changing.
firm[2] a business company.
kind[1] sort or variety.
kind[2] ready to help others.
pick[1] a heavy metal tool with a pointed end.
pick[2] to choose or select.

tire[1] to be unable to go on because of a need for rest.
tire[2] rubber tube filled with air on a wheel.

A Visit from My Grandfather

My grandfather has just retired from his business __(1)__. Over the weekend, he helped us get the garden ready for spring planting. He used a heavy __(2)__ to break up thick clumps of soil. Then each of us chose one __(3)__ of vegetable to plant. This hard work didn't __(4)__ him out.

One night we looked through magazines to find pictures of food for a science display. He would __(5)__ out the pictures with long shears while my job was to __(6)__ the ones I liked best. He showed me a neat way to __(7)__ the pictures together. Another night he helped me fix a flat __(8)__ on my bicycle. It is wonderful having such a __(9)__ visitor, and I know he will always be a __(10)__ friend.

(1) _____   (5) _____

(2) _____   (6) _____

(3) _____   (7) _____   (9) _____

(4) _____   (8) _____   (10) _____

Name _____

Hint Every dictionary has a pronunciation key that shows various spellings for different sounds.

EXAMPLE The beginning sound of *choir* is *k* as in *keep*. Find *k* in the first column and look over to the next column to find words that have different spellings of the /k/ sound. After you find the correct letter combinations for the beginning of a word, you should be able to find the word.

PRONUNCIATION KEY

consonant sounds

d	no**d**, ri**dd**le, call**ed**	m	**d**ru**m**, **d**rummer, li**mb**, hy**mn**, cal**m**
f	**f**ix, di**ff**erent, lau**gh**, **ph**one, cal**f**	n	**n**ear, di**nn**er, **gn**ome, **kn**eel, **pn**eumonia
g	**g**ive, e**gg**, **gh**ost, **gu**ard	ñg	lo**ng**, thi**nk**, to**ng**ue
h	**h**er, **wh**o	p	ho**p**, di**pp**er
j	**j**am, **g**em, exa**gg**erate, gra**du**ate, sol**di**er, ju**dg**ment, a**dj**ust	r	**r**iver, be**rr**y, **rh**yme, **wr**ong
k	**k**ite, wal**k**, **c**an, a**cc**ount, **ch**rome, lu**ck**, la**cqu**er, bis**cu**it, li**qu**or	s	**s**it, mi**ss**, **sc**ience, **c**ent, **ps**ychology, **sch**ism
l	**l**eave, ca**ll**, is**l**and		

Directions Use the pronunciation key above to help you circle the correct spelling. You may also need to check a dictionary.

1. Find a word that rhymes with pail and means "a small wild bird."

   quail   kwail   chwail

2. Find a word that rhymes with ham and means "a baby sheep."

   lam   lamb   lalm

3. Find a word that rhymes with best and means "a visitor."

   gest   ghest   guest

4. Find a word that rhymes with bat and means "a small flying insect."

   gnat   nat   pant

5. Find a word that rhymes with string and means "to twist with force."

   rhing   wring   ring

6. Find a word that rhymes with went and means "a smell, an odor."

   cent   sent   scent

LESSON 85: Different spellings for the same sound

Dictionary tip
The dictionary can help you spell and figure out the meaning of a word. The dictionary can also help you pronounce a word.

MORE DICTIONARY TIPS
The **respelling** that follows a dictionary entry shows you how to pronounce the word. The dictionary **pronunciation key** can help you pronounce each sound shown in the respelling.

SYMBOL	KEY WORDS	SYMBOL	KEY WORDS	SYMBOL	KEY WORDS
b	**b**ed, du**b**	m	**m**et, tri**m**	y	**y**et, **y**ard
d	**d**id, ha**d**	n	**n**ot, to**n**	z	**z**ebra, ha**z**e
f	**f**all, o**ff**	p	**p**ut, ta**p**	ch	**ch**in, ar**ch**
g	**g**et, do**g**	r	**r**ed, dea**r**	ng	ri**ng**, si**ng**er
h	**h**e, a**h**ead	s	**s**ell, pa**ss**	sh	**sh**e, da**sh**
j	**j**oy, **j**ump	t	**t**op, ha**t**	th	**th**in, tru**th**
k	**k**ill, ba**k**e	v	**v**at, ha**v**e	_th_	**th**en, fa**th**er
l	**l**et, ba**ll**	w	**w**ill, al**w**ays	zh	**s** in plea**s**ure as in (āb 'l)

Directions Study the consonant sounds taken from a dictionary pronunciation key. Then read the respellings shown below. Use the pronunciation key to help you identify the matching entry word. Circle the entry word that goes with each respelling.

1. (kat)   kitten   cat   castle
2. (kwik)   quick   kick   quest
3. (duz)   dove   does   dozen
4. (nit)   nitch   knit   knot
5. (laf)   loft   taffy   laugh
6. (hej)   hedge   hip   edge
7. (res´ 'l) rest   wrestle restless
8. (haf)   half   hall   hand
9. (jim)   jimmy   gym   jet

Directions Use the pronunciation key to write the sound symbols for the underlined letters in the words.

1. ba**g**el _____   2. trea**s**ure _____   3. cir**c**us _____

4. ri**ng** _____   5. ba**ss** _____   6. la**b**el _____

7. **sh**out _____   8. Su**n**day _____   9. fet**ch** _____

LESSON 85: The pronunciation key

Name _____

Directions Study the long and short vowel sounds from a dictionary pronunciation key. Pronounce each example word and listen for the vowel sound.

Hint In the last lesson, you worked with the consonant section of a dictionary pronunciation key. Every pronunciation key also has a vowel section.

SYMBOL	KEY WORDS
a	a**sk**, f**at**
ā	**ape**, d**ate**
e	**elf**, t**en**
ē	**even**, m**eet**
i	**is**, h**it**
ī	**ice**, f**ire**
ō	**open**, g**o**
u	**up**, c**ut**

Directions Read the respellings below. Notice the symbols in boldface print. Beside each respelling, write the example words from the pronunciation key that show you how to pronounce the symbol. Then write the entry word for each respelling.

1. (tīr) _____ _____

2. (grēt) _____ _____

3. (lāt) _____ _____

4. (mis) _____ _____

5. (stōv) _____ _____

6. (plāt) _____ _____

7. (pas) _____ _____

8. (fus) _____ _____

9. (bred) _____ _____

10. (mīs) _____ _____

11. (bluf) _____ _____

12. (krēm) _____ _____

13. (stik) _____ _____

14. (smel) _____ _____

Directions Study more vowel sounds taken from a dictionary pronunciation key. Pronounce each example word and listen for the vowel sound.

Hint In addition to long and short vowel sounds, the pronunciation key also contains other vowel sounds.

SYMBOL	KEY WORDS
ä	car, lot
er	berry, care
ir	mirror, here
ô	law, horn
oi	oil, point
oo	look, pull
o͞o	ooze, tool
yoo	unite, cure
yo͞o	cute, few
ou	out, crowd
ur	fur, fern

Directions Use the pronunciation key to help you say each respelling. Then write each word from the word box on the line beside its respelling.

cart	cartoon	lot	word	clause
round	loss	purr	close	heir
room	lose	car	purse	hair

1. (klôz) _____

2. (kär) _____

3. (ro͞om) _____

4. (wurd) _____

5. (purs) _____

6. (lôs) _____

7. (her) _____

8. (kärt) _____

9. (lät) _____

10. (lo͞oz) _____

LESSON 86: The pronunciation key

Name _____

Hint In a word with two or more syllables, one syllable is **accented** or **stressed** more than the others. In the dictionary, an accent mark (´) is placed after the syllable that is said with more stress.

EXAMPLES

dā´ līt (daylight)
i las´ tik (elastic)
den´ tist (dentist)

Directions For each word below, the respelling is shown. Place the accent mark where it belongs. You may check your dictionary, if necessary.

1. iceboat (īs bōt)

2. deny (di nī)

3. obey (ō bā)

4. relieve (ri lēv)

5. ruin (r o͞o in)

6. event (i vent)

Directions Read each sentence. Circle the respelling of the underlined word that makes sense in the sentence.

Hint Sometimes a word can be pronounce in different ways depending on its meaning. In this case, the accent may shift to another syllable.

1. Olivia's favorite birthday present was a new bike.

prez´ 'nt
pri zent´

2. She also liked the record of her favorite song.

ri kôrd´
rek´ ərd

3. Her sister gave her a puzzle with a picture of a sandy desert.

di zʉrt´
dez´ ərt

4. Her big project now is to write thank you notes.

präj´ ekt
prə jekt´

Directions Read the words in the list below. Then use the respelling clues at the bottom of the page to help you solve the crossword puzzle.

snack	light	guess	kayak	wreckage	wrap	groan
rough	hour	seize	some	solid	gem	ape
clear	ear	earth	rocket	rocks	smudge	small
knee	her	electric	charcoal	chalk	stick	

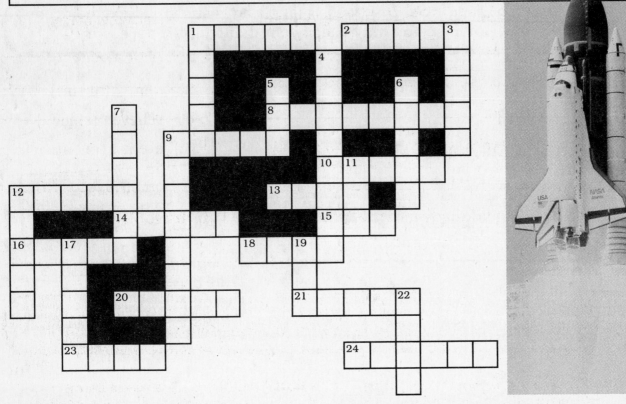

Across

1. sēz
2. räks
8. i lek′ trik
9. klir
10. kī′ ak
12. snak
13. rap
14. ᵾrth
15. jem
16. līt
18. nē
20. chôk
21. ruf
23. sum
24. smuj

Down

1. smôl
3. stik
4. rek′ ij
5. hᵾr
6. grōn
7. räk′ it
9. chär′ kōl
11. āp
12. säl′ əd
17. ges
19. ir
22. our

174

LESSON 87: Review dictionary skills

Name _____

Directions Look at the words in the box. List them under the correct pair of dictionary guide words. Then read the sentences and write the underlined words in the order in which they appear in the dictionary.

fury	gable	fume	gallant	funnel
gadfly	gamble	furious	gaily	

fulfill/furnace   **further/gadget**   **gaggle/game**

_____   _____   _____

_____   _____   _____

_____   _____   _____

1. The joyful jester juggled and jauntily danced a jig.

_____ _____ _____ _____

2. The laughing landlady laid the latchkey on the laundry table.

_____ _____ _____ _____

Directions Read the dictionary page. Then use the entry words to complete the sentences. Be sure to write the number of the definition.

note (nōt) **n.** **1** a short letter. **2** an official promise to pay money. **3** a musical tone.

organ (ôr′gən) **n.** **1** a musical instrument that sends air through pipes. **2** a part of an animal or plant that has some special purpose.

outlet (out′let) **n.** **1** a way of using up. **2** a store that sells the goods of a certain manufacturer.

pitch (pich) **n.** **1** anything tossed or thrown. **2** the highness or lowness of a musical tone.

1. David took lessons and learned to play the _____.

2. It's a good _____ for his musical talent.

3. He practiced a new song and can play every _____.

4. It helps that he has perfect _____.

droop (drōop)   **1** to sink, hang, or bend down.   **2** to become weak, sad, tired.

dust•er (dust′ər)   **1** A cloth or brush used for getting dust off.   **2** a short, lightweight housecoat.

fend•er (fen′dər)   **1** a metal piece over the wheel of a car.   **2** a metal piece at the front of a train.   **3** a low screen or frame in front of an open fireplace.

flick•er (flik′ər)   **1** to burn or shine in a way that is not clear or steady.   **2** to move in a quick, unsteady way.

flick•er² (flik′ər)   a woodpecker of North America with a red mark on the head, and wings colored golden underneath.

guar•an•tee (gar ən tē′)   **1** a promise to replace something that does not work or last as long as it should.   **2** a promise that something will be done.

guf•faw (gə fô′)   a loud rough laugh.

han•dle (han′d'l)   **1** to hold or touch with the hand.   **2** to take care of, manage, or control.   **3** to deal with; treat.

1. Circle the words that come before <u>handle</u> in alphabetical order.

hair   happy   hazel   haggard

hammock   halfback   hamster   hasty

2. Circle the guide words that would be on the same page as <u>guarantee</u>.

guppy/gym   gruel/guidance   group/Guam

3. Write the entry words from the top of the page that are homographs.

_____   _____

4. Write the entry word that has one syllable. _____

5. Write the entry words in which the last syllable is stressed or accented.

_____   _____

____ 1. The fire only **flickered** because it needed more wood.

____ 2. The ashes were piled nearly to the top of the **fender.**

____ 3. Phil **guaranteed** that he would clean out the ashes tomorrow.

____ 4. It wouldn't be safe to **handle** the hot coals tonight.